Glencoe Science

Biology

Unit 5 Resources
Bacteria, Viruses, Protists, and Fungi

Glencoe

New York, New York   Columbus, Ohio   Chicago, Illinois

A GLENCOE PROGRAM
BIOLOGY

 biologygmh.com

Check out the following features on your **Online Learning Center:**

Study Tools

- Interactive Tables
- Interactive Time Line
- Animated illustrations
- National Geographic Visualizing animations

Self-Check Quizzes
Chapter Tests
Standardized Test Practice
Vocabulary PuzzleMaker
Interactive Tutor
Multilingual Science Glossary
Study to Go
Online Student Edition

Extensions

Virtual Labs
Microscopy Links
Periodic Table Links
Career Links
Web Links
WebQuest Projects
Science Fair Ideas
Internet BioLabs

For Teachers

Teacher Forum
Teaching Today, and much more!

Mc Graw Hill Glencoe

The **McGraw·Hill** Companies

Copyright © by The McGraw-Hill Companies, Inc. All rights reserved. Permission is granted to reproduce the material contained herein on the condition that such material be reproduced only for classroom use; be provided to students, teachers, and families without charge; and be used solely in conjunction with the *Glencoe Biology* program. Any other reproduction, for use or sale, is prohibited without prior written permission of the publisher.

Send all inquiries to:
Glencoe/McGraw-Hill
8787 Orion Place
Columbus, OH 43240-4027

ISBN 13: 978-0-07-874609-3
ISBN 10: 0-07-874609-4

Printed in the United States of America

4 5 6 7 8 9 10 MAL 11 10

Copyright © Glencoe/McGraw-Hill, a division of The McGraw-Hill Companies, Inc.

Table of Contents

Copyright © Glencoe/McGraw-Hill, a division of The McGraw-Hill Companies, Inc.

To the Teacher

This unit-based booklet contains resource materials to help you teach this unit more effectively. You will find the following in the chapters:

Reproducible Pages

Hands-on Activities

Launch Lab, MiniLab, and BioLab Worksheets: Each activity in this book is an expanded version of each lab that appears in the Student Edition of *Glencoe Biology*. All materials lists, procedures, and questions are repeated so that students can read and complete a lab in most cases without having a textbook on the lab table. All lab questions are reprinted with lines on which students can write their answers. In addition, for student safety, all appropriate safety symbols and caution statements have been reproduced on these expanded pages. Answer pages for each Launch Lab, MiniLab, and BioLab are included in the *Teacher Guide and Answers* section at the back of this book.

Real-World Biology: These two-page activities provide students with the opportunity to explore a technological or everyday application of biology. There are two types of Real-World Biology pages: Lab activities and Analysis activities. Each activity is directly related to a major concept in the Student Edition, and several examine principles from the physical sciences that underlie the biology content. While some activities are more hands-on, all require critical thinking and creativity. The teaching notes in the *Teacher Guide and Answers* section at the back of this book suggest chapters and topics with which to correlate the activities, explain the purpose of each activity, present career applications for the relevant field of science, offer materials tips and safety tips for the Lab activities, provide teaching strategies that include ideas for below-level and above-level students, and give answers to all questions on the student pages.

Extension and Intervention

Diagnostic Test: Each Diagnostic Test provides an opportunity for students to predict answers to questions about the chapter content based on what they already know. The students decide on one of the possible answers given, and then explain their reasoning. Answers to the questions and explanations for student preconceptions are given in the *Teacher Guide and Answers* section. These student predictions to the questions will allow you to design your lessons to meet the students' needs.

Enrichment: *Enrichment* pages offer research activities to students who need additional challenges. There are three types of *Enrichment* activities: Diagramming, Analyze a Problem, and Group Project. Diagramming activities have students use resources to draw and label their own diagrams. Analyze a Problem activities have students research, discuss, and write about specific topics. Group Project activities have students work in groups to research topics, organize information, and make class presentations.

Copyright © Glencoe/McGraw-Hill, a division of The McGraw-Hill Companies, Inc.

Concept Mapping: The *Concept Mapping* worksheets reinforce and extend the graphic organizational skills introduced in the Skill Handbook in the Student Edition. Concept maps are visual representations of relationships among particular concepts. By using these worksheets, students will gain experience with six different types of concept maps: the network tree, which shows causal information, group hierarchies, and branching procedures; the flowchart, which is similar to an events chain but has more possibilities for events; the cycle map, which shows a series of events without a final outcome; the Venn diagram, which illustrates similarities and differences between items; the events chain, which describes the stages of a process, the steps in a linear procedure, or a sequence of events; and the cycle map, which shows how a series of events interacts to produce a set of results again and again.

There is one *Concept Mapping* worksheet for each chapter in the Student Edition. Each worksheet is geared toward a specific section or sections in the chapter so that you can assign it at the most relevant time. An entire section or just a few key concepts from the section might be mapped. Answers to all *Concept Mapping* worksheets are provided in the *Teacher Guide and Answers* section at the back of this book.

Study Guide in English and Spanish: These pages help students understand, organize, and compare the main biology concepts in the textbook. The questions and activities also help build strong study and reading skills. There are four study guide pages for each chapter. Students will find these pages easy to follow because the section titles match those in the textbook. Italicized sentences in the study guide direct students to the related topics in the text.

The *Study Guide* exercises employ a variety of formats including multiple-choice, matching, true/false, ordering, labeling, completion, and short answer questions. The clear, easy-to-follow exercises and the self-pacing format are geared to build your students' confidence in understanding biology. The English pages are followed immediately by the study guide pages in Spanish.

Section Quick Check: The *Section Quick Check* pages provide students an overview of the text using a short-answer format. Each page of questions is correlated to a section of the Student Edition, and the items are different from those in the Student Edition for broader coverage of section content. The questions utilize Bloom's verbs and are scaffolded according to difficulty from easiest to hardest.

Chapter Tests: The Chapter Tests are arranged in five parts with five different types of questions. These worksheets provide materials to assess your students understanding of concepts from each chapter in the unit.

- Test A (below level): Multiple Choice, Matching, Interpreting, Short Answer, and Concept Application

- Test B (on level): Multiple Choice, Matching and Completion, Interpreting, Short Answer, and Concept Application

- Test C (above level): Multiple Choice, Matching and Completion, Interpreting, Short Answer, and Concept Application

Copyright © Glencoe/McGraw-Hill, a division of The McGraw-Hill Companies, Inc.

The *Multiple Choice, Matching,* and *Completion* questions test comprehension of the vocabulary of the chapter.

The *Interpreting* questions ask the student to combine factual and explanatory information. Students will need to interpret data and discover relationships presented in graphs, tables, and diagrams.

The *Short Answer* questions allow the student to express understanding of the information. Students will apply their understanding of concepts to solve problems, compare and contrast situations, make inferences or predictions, and explain their reasoning.

The *Concept Application* questions present the student with a situation. These situations give the student the opportunity to demonstrate both reasoning and creative skills.

Student Recording Sheet: Student Recording Sheets allow students to use the Chapter Assessment and the Standardized Test Practice questions in the Student Edition as a practice for standardized tests. Student Recording Sheets give them the opportunity to use bubble answer grids and numbers grids for recording answers. Answers for the Student Recording Sheets can be found in the Teacher Wraparound Edition on *Chapter Assessment* and *Standardized Test Practice* pages.

Teacher Guide and Answers: Answers or possible answers for questions in this booklet can be found in the *Teacher Guide and Answers* section. Materials, teaching strategies, and content background, along with chapter references, are also provided where appropriate.

Copyright © Glencoe/McGraw-Hill, a division of The McGraw-Hill Companies, Inc.

Teacher Approval Initials

_____

Date of Approval

Student Lab Safety Form

Student Name: _____

Date: _____

Lab Title: _____

In order to show your teacher that you understand the safety concerns of this lab, the following questions must be answered after the teacher explains the information to you. You must have your teacher initial this form before you can proceed with the lab.

1. How would you describe what you will be doing during this lab?

2. What are the safety concerns associated with this lab (as explained by your teacher)?

- _____
- _____
- _____
- _____
- _____

3. What additional safety concerns or questions do you have?

Copyright © Glencoe/McGraw-Hill, a division of The McGraw-Hill Companies, Inc.

Adapted from Gerlovich, et al. (2004). The Total Science Safety System CD, JaKel, Inc.
Used with Permission.

Table of Contents

Chapter 18 Bacteria and Viruses

Copyright © Glencoe/McGraw-Hill, a division of The McGraw-Hill Companies, Inc.

Diagnostic Test

Bacteria and Viruses

Before reading Chapter 18, predict answers to questions about the chapter content based on what you already know. Circle the letter of the correct answer, and then explain your reasoning.

1. Rance visits a doctor and learns he has a bacterial infection for which the doctor prescribes an antibiotic. Rance asks the doctor what the bacteria look like, and the doctor shows him a photograph of the bacteria. Which does Rance observe in the photo?

   A. a small nucleus with a thin membrane

   B. complex organelles such as mitochondria

   C. fragments of RNA but no DNA strands

   D. long, whiplike structures called flagella

   Explain.

   _____

   _____

   _____

2. Cheryl tells her friend a fact she learned during science class. She explains that a spoonful of soil contains billions of bacteria. Cheryl's friend calls the bacteria disgusting germs, and she wishes all bacteria would become extinct. Cheryl explains the importance of soil bacteria to her friend. Which does she tell her friend?

   A. Bacteria in soil absorb water and transfer it to tree roots.

   B. Soil bacteria decompose dead organisms into vital nutrients.

   C . The bacteria in soil are a major food source for invertebrates.

   D. Without soil bacteria, soil organisms could not digest food.

   Explain.

   _____

   _____

   _____

3. During health class, Juanita learns about common diseases caused by viral infections. About what diseases does she learn?

   _____

   _____

   _____

Copyright © Glencoe/McGraw-Hill, a division of The McGraw-Hill Companies, Inc.

Launch Lab

What are the differences between animal cells and bacterial cells?

You are already familiar with animal cells. How do animal cells compare to the cells of bacteria? Bacteria are the most common organisms in your environment. In fact, billions of bacteria live on and in your body. Many species of bacteria can cause diseases. What makes bacteria different from your own cells?

Procedure

1. Read and complete the lab safety form.

2. Use a **compound light microscope** to observe the slides of **animal and bacterial cells.**

3. Complete a data table listing the similarities and differences between the two types of cells.

Data and Observations

Analysis

1. **Describe** the different cells you observed. What did you notice about each?

_____

_____

2. **Infer** whether they are living things. What leads you to these conclusions?

_____

_____

_____

Copyright © Glencoe/McGraw-Hill, a division of The McGraw-Hill Companies, Inc.

MiniLab

CHAPTER 18
Classify Bacteria

What types of characteristics are used to divide bacteria into groups? Bacteria can be stained to show the differences in peptidoglycan (PG) in their cell walls. Based on this difference in their cell walls, bacteria are divided into two main groups.

Procedure

1. Read and complete the lab safety form.
2. Choose four different **slides of bacteria** that have been stained to show cell wall differences. The slides will be labeled with the names of the bacteria and marked either *thick PG layer* or *thin PG layer*.

3. Use the oil immersion lens of your **microscope** to observe the four slides.
4. Record all of your observations, including those about the cell color, in a table.

Data and Observations

Analysis

1. **Interpret Data** Based on your observations, make a hypothesis about how to differentiate between the two groups of bacteria.

_____

_____

_____

2. **Describe** two different cell shapes you saw on the slides you observed.

_____

_____

_____

Copyright © Glencoe/McGraw-Hill, a division of The McGraw-Hill Companies, Inc.

Design Your Own
BioLab

CHAPTER 18
How can the most effective antibiotics be determined?

Background: A patient is suffering from a serious bacterial infection, and as the doctor, you must choose from several new antibiotics to treat the infection.

Question: *How can the effectiveness of antibiotics be tested?*

Materials
Choose materials that would be appropriate for this lab. Possible materials include:
bacteria cultures
sterile nutrient agar
petri dishes
antibiotic disks
control disks
forceps

Bunsen burner
marking pen
long-handle cotton swabs
70% ethanol
thermometer
pot
disinfectant
autoclave disposal bag

Safety Precautions 🥽 🧤 ☣ 🚫 🖐
🖐

WARNING: *Clean your work area with disinfectant after you finish.*

Plan and Perform the Experiment
1. Read and complete the lab safety form.
2. Design an experiment to test the effectiveness of different antibiotics. Identify the controls and variables in your experiment.
3. Create a data table for recording your observations and measurements.
4. Make sure your teacher approves your plan before you proceed.
5. Conduct your experiment.
6. **Cleanup and Disposal** Dispose of all materials according to your teacher's instructions. Disinfect your area.

Data and Observations

Copyright © Glencoe/McGraw-Hill, a division of The McGraw-Hill Companies, Inc.

Analyze and Conclude

1. Compare and Contrast What are the effects of the different antibiotics for the
bacteria species you tested?

_____

_____

_____

2. Hypothesize Why would a doctor instruct you to take all of your prescribed
antibiotics for a bacterial infection even if you start feeling better before the pills
run out?

_____

_____

3. Explain What were the limitations of your experimental design?

_____

_____

4. Error Analysis Compare and contrast the observations and measurements collected
by your group with the data from the experiments designed by other groups.
Identify possible sources of error in your experimental data.

_____

_____

Copyright © Glencoe/McGraw-Hill, a division of The McGraw-Hill Companies, Inc.

Real-World Biology: Analysis

CHAPTER 18
Prion Diseases

Many people live in areas where they never see deer. However, there are some areas that are overpopulated with deer. An overpopulation of deer can be harmful to people and to the deer. For example, in urban areas the number of car accidents involving deer increases. An overpopulation of deer is also harmful to ecosystems because deer feed on plants. As deer run out of plants to eat, they begin to starve. A high concentration of deer in an area also makes the deer more susceptible to diseases.

One disease that concerns scientists and hunters is chronic wasting disease (CWD) in deer and elk. It is classified as a transmissible spongiform encephalopathy (TSE), which is caused by prions and affects the animal's brain. Other TSEs, or prion diseases, include scrapie in sheep, bovine spongiform encephalopathy (mad cow disease) in cattle, and Creutzfeldt-Jacob disease in humans. Prion diseases are fatal. In this activity, you will analyze information about the spread of CWD and what is being done to try to prevent its spread.

Part A: The Spread of Chronic Wasting Disease

Chronic wasting disease was first reported as a wasting syndrome in captive deer in a Colorado research facility in the late 1960s. Deer with this disease had a change in behavior and appearance. Among other symptoms, they lost weight, stumbled, ground their teeth, and had tremors. They all died from the disease. Then CWD was reported in a Wyoming research facility. In 1978, the disease was recognized as a transmissible spongiform encephalopathy.

The table below summarizes information about the spread of CWD in deer and elk since the late 1960s. When cases of CWD are found in a new area, the evidence suggests that people have moved captive animals to farms or other facilities without knowing the animals were diseased. If animals with CWD escape into the wild, they transmit the disease to animals living in the area. CWD was transmitted to Wisconsin deer in this way. In other states, such as New Mexico, the origin of the disease is not known.

Date	Location of Animals with CWD
Late 1960s to 1980	disease found in deer and elk in research facilities in Colorado and Wyoming
1981	first known occurrence of CWD in wild animals; wild deer and elk in Colorado found with CWD
1985	disease found in wild deer and elk in Wyoming
1990s	northeastern Colorado and southeastern Wyoming described as an endemic area for CWD, meaning that animals with the disease are confined to this specific area
1996 to 2000	CWD diagnosed in farmed elk herds in Colorado, Kansas, Montana, Nebraska, Oklahoma, and South Dakota
2001	a wild mule deer in Nebraska found with CWD; the area of animals with CDW extended into southwestern Nebraska
2000 to 2002	CWD found in wild deer in northwestern Nebraska, southern New Mexico, southwestern South Dakota, south-central Wisconsin, and northwestern Colorado

Copyright © Glencoe/McGraw-Hill, a division of The McGraw-Hill Companies, Inc.

Analyze and Conclude

Respond to each question.

1. **Summarize** How would you describe the spread of CWD in the last 40 years?

   _____

   _____

2. **Suggest** What suggestions would you make for preventing the spread of CWD to states that are not near any current cases of CWD?

   _____

   _____

Part B: Concerns About Chronic Wasting Disease

Scientists know how most diseases caused by bacteria and viruses are transmitted. However, they do not know exactly how diseases caused by prions are transmitted. Evidence suggests that prion diseases are passed from one animal to another. Sheep get scrapie from other sheep. Deer and elk get CWD from other deer and elk. Scientists are working to determine whether prions in soil, water, or an animal's food can transmit CWD.

Scientists do know that body parts from sheep, some of which had scrapie, were used to manufacture food for cows. Cows that ate this contaminated food developed mad cow disease. People can develop Creutzfeldt-Jacob disease if they eat contaminated meat from these cows. At the present time, the risk of CWD being transmitted to humans is low. No known cases exist. But the increasing spread of the disease does increase the exposure that humans have to the disease. More research needs to be done before scientists fully understand CWD.

Analyze and Conclude

Respond to each question.

1. **Apply** Some areas have laws that prohibit people from feeding wild deer. How might these laws help prevent the spread of CWD?

   _____

   _____

2. **Recommend** Deer and elk can have CWD for years before they show any symptoms. Tests can indicate the presence of the disease before symptoms are noticeable. Based on what is known about transmission of other prion diseases, what would you recommend for people who hunt deer or elk for food?

   _____

   _____

   _____

CAREERS IN BIOLOGY

Wildlife Biology Visit biologygmh.com for information on wildlife disease experts. What are the responsibilities of a wildlife disease expert?

Copyright © Glencoe/McGraw-Hill, a division of The McGraw-Hill Companies, Inc.

CHAPTER 18

Enrichment

Analyze a Problem: Human Bacterial and Viral Diseases

Many bacteria and viruses do not cause disease in humans. However, each year millions of people around the world are affected by bacterial and viral diseases. Scientists work to understand the causes and symptoms of these diseases and how they are transmitted. This information helps to develop vaccines, antibiotics, and antiviral drugs to combat the wide variety of human bacterial and viral diseases.

Select The table below lists 12 human diseases that are caused by a bacterium or virus. Select one of the diseases to research.

Research Once you have selected a disease, research information about it. Questions to consider while researching the disease include: What are the symptoms of the disease? How is it transmitted? Is the disease infectious? Are there any vaccines or treatments available? Where does the disease commonly occur? Have there been any important historical outbreaks of the disease?

Discuss Use your textbook and other reference materials to find information. Discuss your topic and possible answers to your questions with your teacher and classmates.

Write Finally, based on your research and class discussion, write an article about the disease you selected. Provide answers for any questions you researched and discussed. Be sure to properly cite the sources you used to write your article.

Disease	Pathogen	Pathogen Type
Anthrax	*Bacillus anthracis*	bacterium
Chicken pox	varicella	virus
Ebola	filovirus	virus
Gas gangrene	*Clostridium perfringens*	bacterium
Mumps	paramyxovirus	virus
Pneumonic plague	*Yersinia pestis*	bacterium
Smallpox	variola	virus
Rabies	rhabdovirus	virus
Tetanus	*Clostridium tetani*	bacterium
Tuberculosis	*Mycobacterium tuberculosis*	bacterium
Whooping cough	*Bordetella pertussis*	bacterium
Yellow fever	flavivirus	virus

Copyright © Glencoe/McGraw-Hill, a division of The McGraw-Hill Companies, Inc.

Concept Mapping

CHAPTER 18
Viral Infections

Complete the events chain about how the lytic cycle and lysogenic cycle in viral infections are related. These terms may be used more than once: cytoplasm, dormant, exocytosis, genetic material, host cell, host cell chromosome, lysogenic cycle, lytic cycle, protein coat, viral genes.

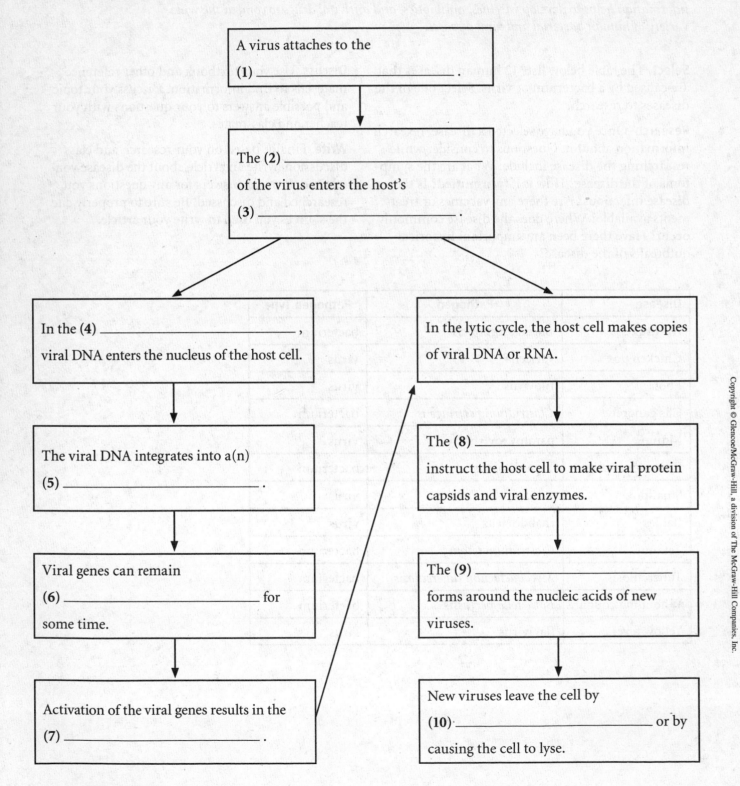

A virus attaches to the

(1) _____.

The (2) _____

of the virus enters the host's

(3) _____.

In the (4) _____,
viral DNA enters the nucleus of the host cell.

In the lytic cycle, the host cell makes copies of viral DNA or RNA.

The viral DNA integrates into a(n)

(5) _____.

The (8) _____
instruct the host cell to make viral protein capsids and viral enzymes.

Viral genes can remain

(6) _____ for

some time.

The (9) _____
forms around the nucleic acids of new viruses.

Activation of the viral genes results in the

(7) _____.

New viruses leave the cell by

(10) _____ or by

causing the cell to lyse.

Copyright © Glencoe/McGraw-Hill, a division of The McGraw-Hill Companies, Inc.

Study Guide

CHAPTER 18

Section 1: Bacteria

In your textbook, read about the diversity of prokaryotes.

Respond to each statement.

1. **State** one way in which eubacteria and archaebacteria are different and one way in which they are the same.

   _____

   _____

   _____

2. **State** one way in which thermoacidophiles and halophiles are different and one way in which they are the same.

   _____

   _____

   _____

In your textbook, read about prokaryote structure.

Label the diagram of the bacterial cell. Use these choices:

capsule	cell wall	chromosome
flagella	pili	plasma membrane

3. _____

4. _____

5. _____

6. _____

7. _____

8. _____

Copyright © Glencoe/McGraw-Hill, a division of The McGraw-Hill Companies, Inc.

In your textbook, read about prokaryote structure, identifying prokaryotes, and survival of bacteria.

Match the definition in Column A with the term in Column B.

Column A		Column B
_____	9. part of the composition of the cell walls of eubacteria	**A.** nucleoid
_____	10. dormant bacterial cell	**B.** plasmid
_____	11. area of prokaryotic cell containing a large circular chromosome	**C.** peptidoglycan
_____	12. small circular DNA in prokaryotic cell	**D.** endospore

Complete the table below by drawing each type of prokaryote.

Cocci	Bacilli	Spirochetes
13.	14.	15.

In your textbook, read about the ecology of bacteria.

Use each of the terms below only once to complete the passage.

antibiotics	bacteria	decomposers	disease
nitrogen	nitrogen fixation	normal flora	symbiotically
vitamin K	yogurt		

Most (16) _____ are beneficial. Some bacteria are

(17) _____ that return vital nutrients to the environment. Certain types of

bacteria use (18) _____ gas directly and convert this gas into compounds that

plants can use. This process is called (19) _____ . Some bacteria called

(20) _____ live in and on the human body. *Escherichia coli* live

(21) _____ in the gut of humans and produce

(22) _____ , which humans need for blood clotting. Many food

products, such as cheese and (23) _____ , are made with the aid of bacteria.

Other bacteria make (24) _____ . A small percentage of bacteria can cause

(25) _____ .

Copyright © Glencoe/McGraw-Hill, a division of The McGraw-Hill Companies, Inc.

Study Guide

In your textbook, read about viruses and viral infection.

Match the definition in Column A with the term in Column B.

Column A	Column B
_____ 1. genetic material of a virus	**A.** virus
_____ 2. where a virus attaches to a host cell	**B.** bacteriophage
_____ 3. nonliving particle that replicates inside a living cell	**C.** DNA or RNA
_____ 4. outer layer of virus made of proteins	**D.** capsid
_____ 5. nervous system disease	**E.** AIDS
_____ 6. a virus that infects bacteria	**F.** rabies
_____ 7. a cell in which a virus replicates	**G.** host
_____ 8. a virus that is spread through sexual contact	**H.** receptor site

Complete the table by checking the correct column(s) for each description.

Description	Lytic Cycle	Lysogenic Cycle
9. Viral genes are expressed immediately after the virus infects the host cell.		
10. Many new viruses are assembled.		
11. This cycle is preceded by a virus entering a host cell.		
12. Viral DNA is integrated into the host cell's chromosome.		
13. Viruses are released from the host cell by lysis or exocytosis.		
14. The viral genes can remain dormant for months or years.		

Copyright © Glencoe/McGraw-Hill, a division of The McGraw-Hill Companies, Inc.

In your textbook, read about retroviruses.

Use each of the terms below only once to complete the passage.

cancer-causing	DNA	host cell	human immunodeficiency virus (HIV)
nucleus	retrovirus	reverse transcriptase	RNA

Some disease-causing viruses have (15) _____ instead of DNA. This type of

virus is called a (16) _____ . The best-known virus of this type is

(17) _____ . Some (18) _____ viruses belong to this

group. In the core of the virus is RNA and an enzyme called (19) _____ , which

is the enzyme that transcribes (20) _____ from viral RNA. Then DNA moves

into the (21) _____ of a cell, and the (22) _____

manufactures and assembles new HIV particles.

In your textbook, read about viruses and prions.

Complete the table by checking the correct column(s) for each description.

Description	Viruses	Prions
23. Made of a protein		
24. Replicate in cells of organisms		
25. Made of a nonliving strand of genetic material		
26. Normally live in cells		
27. Cause infection and disease		
28. Cause proteins to mutate		
29. Attach to host cell and enter the cytoplasm		

If the statement is true, write true. *If the statement is false, replace the italicized term or phrase to make it true.*

30. Mutated prions are shaped like a *rod.*

_____

31. A disease in cattle associated with prions is *mad cow disease.*

_____

32. Abnormal prions cause nerve cells in the *heart* to burst.

_____

Copyright © Glencoe/McGraw-Hill, a division of The McGraw-Hill Companies, Inc.

Guía de estudio

En tu libro de texto, lee acerca de la diversidad de las procariotas.

Responde a cada afirmación.

1. **Indica** una manera en la cual las eubacterias y las arqueobacterias se diferencian y otra manera en la cual se asemejan.

_____

_____

_____

2. **Indica** una manera en la cual los termoacidófilos y los halófilos se diferencian y otra manera en la cual se asemejan.

_____

_____

_____

En tu libro de texto, lee acerca de la estructura de las procariotas.

Identifica el diagrama de la célula bacterial. Usa estas opciones:

| cápsula | cromosoma | flagelos |
| pared celular | membrana plasmática | pelos |

3. _____

4. _____

5. _____

6. _____

7. _____

8. _____

Copyright © Glencoe/McGraw-Hill, a division of The McGraw-Hill Companies, Inc.

En tu libro de texto, lee acerca de la estructura de las procariotas, la identificación de las procariotas y la supervivencia de las bacterias.

Relaciona la definición de la columna A con el término de la columna B.

Columna A	Columna B
_____ 9. parte de la composición de las paredes celulares de las eubacterias	**A.** nucleoide
_____ 10. célula bacterial latenteo	**B.** plásmido
_____ 11. área de una célula procariótica que contiene un cromosoma circular grande	**C.** peptidoglicano
	D. endospora
_____ 12. ADN circular pequeño en una célula procariótica	

Completa la siguiente tabla con el dibujo de cada tipo de procariota.

Cocos	Bacilos	Espiroquetas
13.	14.	15.

En tu libro de texto, lee acerca de la ecología de las bacterias.

Usa cada uno de los siguientes términos sólo una vez para completar el párrafo.

antibióticos	bacterias	descomponedores	enfermedades
fijación de nitrógeno	flora normal	nitrógeno	simbióticamente
vitamina K	yogurt		

La mayoría de las (16) _____ brindan beneficios. Algunas bacterias son

(17) _____ que devuelven nutrientes vitales al ambiente. Ciertos tipos de

bacterias usan el gas (18) _____ directamente y convierten este gas en

compuestos que las plantas pueden usar. Este proceso se llama (19) _____ .

Algunas bacterias llamadas (20) _____ viven por dentro y por fuera del cuerpo

humano. La *Escherichia coli* vive (21) _____ en el intestino de los humanos y

produce (22) _____ , la cual es necesaria para los humanos para la coagulación

de la sangre. Muchos productos alimenticios, como el queso y el (23) _____ , se

preparan con la ayuda de bacterias. Otras bacterias producen (24) _____ . Un

pequeño porcentaje de bacteria puede causar (25) _____ .

Copyright © Glencoe/McGraw-Hill, a division of The McGraw-Hill Companies, Inc.

Guía de estudio

En tu libro de texto, lee acerca de los virus y la infección viral.

Relaciona la definición de la columna A con el término de la columna B.

Columna A		Columna B
_____	1. material genético de un virus	**A.** virus
_____	2. donde un virus se adhiere a una célula huésped	**B.** bacteriófago
_____	3. partícula no viviente que se replica dentro de una célula viva	**C.** ADN o ARN
_____	4. capa exterior del virus hecho de proteínas	**D.** cápside
_____	5. enfermedad del sistema nervioso	**E.** SIDA
_____	6. un virus que infecta las bacterias	**F.** rabia
_____	7. una célula en la cual un virus se replica	**G.** huésped
_____	8. un virus que se propaga mediante contacto sexual	**H.** sitio receptor

Completa la tabla marcando la(s) columna(s) correcta(s) para cada descripción.

Descripción	Ciclo lítico	Ciclo lisogénioco
9. Los genes virales se expresan inmediatamente después de que el virus infecta la célula huésped.		
10. Muchos virus nuevos se arman.		
11. Este ciclo está precedido por un virus que entra a una célula huésped.		
12. El ADN viral se integra en el cromosoma de la célula huésped.		
13. Los virus se liberan de la célula huésped mediante el proceso de lisis o exocitosis.		
14. Los genes virales pueden permanecer latentes por meses o años.		

Copyright © Glencoe/McGraw-Hill, a division of The McGraw-Hill Companies, Inc.

Guía de estudio, **Sección 2: Los virus y los priones** continuación

En tu libro de texto, lee acerca de los retrovirus.

Usa cada uno de los siguientes términos sólo una vez para completar el párrafo.

ADN	ARN	causan cáncer	célula huésped
núcleo	virus de inmunodeficiencia humana (VIH)	retrovirus	transcriptasa inversa

Algunos virus que causan enfermedades tienen (15) _____ en vez

de ADN. Este tipo de virus se denomina (16) _____ . El virus de

este tipo más conocido es el (17) _____ . Algunos virus que

(18) _____ pertenecen a este grupo. En el centro del virus se encuentra

el ARN y una enzima llamada (19) _____ , la cual es la enzima que

transcribe el (20) _____ del ARN viral. Luego, el ADN se traslada al

(21) _____ de una célula, y la (22) _____

fabrica y arma nuevas partículas de VIH.

En tu libro de texto, lee acerca de los virus y los priones.

Completa la tabla marcando la(s) columna(s) correcta(s) para cada descripción.

Descripción	Virus	Priones
23. Están hechos de una proteína		
24. Se replican en las células de los organismos		
25. Están hechos de una cadena de material genético no viviente		
26. Normalmente viven en las células		
27. Causan infecciones y enfermedades		
28. Causan que las proteínas muten		
29. Se pegan a la célula huésped y entran al citoplasma		

Si la afirmación es verdadera, escribe «verdadero». Si la afirmación es falsa, substituye el término o la frase en cursiva para volverla verdadera.

30. Los priones mutados tienen forma de *varilla.*

_____

31. Una enfermedad en el ganado relacionada con los priones es la *enfermedad de las vacas locas.*

_____

32. Los priones anormales causan que las células nerviosas en el *corazón* exploten.

_____

Copyright © Glencoe/McGraw-Hill, a division of The McGraw-Hill Companies, Inc.

Section
Quick Check

Section 1: Bacteria

After reading the section in your textbook, respond to each statement.

1. Specify the three ways in which prokaryotes obtain energy for cellular respiration.

_____

_____

_____

_____

2. Discuss the functions of pili.

_____

_____

3. Describe the structure of prokaryotes.

_____

_____

_____

_____

_____

4. Compare and **contrast** eubacteria and archaebacteria.

_____

_____

_____

_____

_____

5. Clarify why creation of endospores is not considered a type of reproduction.

_____

_____

_____

Copyright © Glencoe/McGraw-Hill, a division of The McGraw-Hill Companies, Inc.

Section
Quick Check

After reading the section in your textbook, respond to each statement.

1. Define *prion.*

_____

_____

2. Describe the general structure of a virus.

_____

_____

_____

3. Theorize why viruses are thought to have evolved after cells instead of before.

_____

_____

_____

4. Summarize viral infection of a cell.

_____

_____

_____

_____

5. Distinguish between the lytic cycle and the lysogenic cycle.

_____

_____

_____

_____

Copyright © Glencoe/McGraw-Hill, a division of The McGraw-Hill Companies, Inc.

Chapter Test A

CHAPTER 18

Bacteria and Viruses

Part A: Multiple Choice

In the space at the left, write the letter of the term or phrase that best answers each question.

_____ 1. Which is the meaning of *prokaryote*?
   A. multicellular
   B. unicellular
   C. with a nucleus
   D. without a nucleus

_____ 2. Which is the function of a flagellum?
   A. food production
   B. movement
   C. protein synthesis
   D. reproduction

_____ 3. Which describes most types of viruses?
   A. a small, solid ball of infectious protein
   B. genetic material wrapped in a protein coat
   C. primitive type of bacteria cell
   D. the smallest type of living cell

Part B: Matching

Matching Set 1 *Write the letter of the correct category on the line next to the bacterial disease. Answers may be used only once.*

_____ 1. acne   A. respiratory disease

_____ 2. strep throat   B. sexually transmitted disease

_____ 3. syphilis   C. skin disease

Matching Set 2 *Write the letter of the correct category on the line next to the viral disease. Answers may be used only once.*

_____ 4. AIDS (HIV)   A. respiratory disease

_____ 5. common cold   B. sexually transmitted disease

_____ 6. warts   C. skin disease

Copyright © Glencoe/McGraw-Hill, a division of The McGraw-Hill Companies, Inc.

Chapter Test A CONTINUED

Part C: Interpreting Drawings

*Use **Figure 1** to respond to each statement.*

1. Identify the type of cell represented by **Figure 1.**

_____

2. Identify the cell parts labeled *A* and *B*.

A. _____

B. _____

*Use **Figure 2** to respond to the following statement.*

3. Identify the structure represented by **Figure 2.**

_____

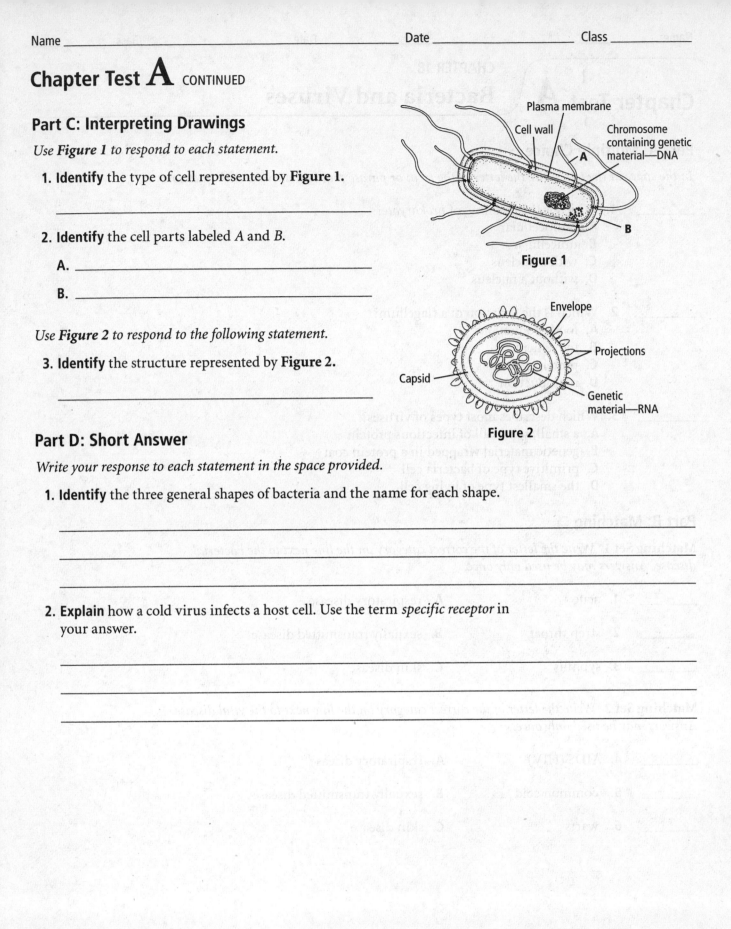

Figure 1

Figure 2

Part D: Short Answer

Write your response to each statement in the space provided.

1. Identify the three general shapes of bacteria and the name for each shape.

_____

_____

_____

2. Explain how a cold virus infects a host cell. Use the term *specific receptor* in your answer.

_____

_____

_____

Copyright © Glencoe/McGraw-Hill, a division of The McGraw-Hill Companies, Inc.

Chapter Test A CONTINUED

Part E: Concept Application

Write your response to each statement in the space provided.

1. **Apply** A person can be infected with a few bacteria cells on one day and feel ill the next day from a bacterial infection. Explain how bacteria cells can infect a person that quickly. Use the term *binary fission* in your answer.

   _____

   _____

   _____

2. **Hypothesize** the effect on a forest ecosystem if all bacteria in the forest become extinct. Use the term *decomposer* in your answer.

   _____

   _____

   _____

Copyright © Glencoe/McGraw-Hill, a division of The McGraw-Hill Companies, Inc.

Chapter Test **B**

CHAPTER 18
Bacteria and Viruses

Part A: Multiple Choice

In the space at the left, write the letter of the term, phrase, or sentence that best answers each question.

_____ 1. Which contrasts eubacteria and archaebacteria?
   A. Archaebacteria live in more extreme habitats.
   B. Eubacteria contain more complex DNA.
   C. Eubacteria have thinner cell walls.
   D. Only archaebacteria have RNA strands.

_____ 2. Which is an advantage of a prokaryote's small size?
   A. able to diffuse nutrients throughout the cell
   B. able to function with small cell mitochondrias
   C. adapted for a smaller surface-to-volume ratio
   D. are not easily located and hunted by predators

_____ 3. Which is an important function of normal flora?
   A. aid with bone marrow production
   B. crowd out pathogenic bacteria
   C. destroy digestive tract pathogens
   D. manufacture iron in the bloodstream

_____ 4. Which is the smallest?
   A. archaebacterium
   B. cold virus
   C. eubacterium
   D. skin cell

_____ 5. Which describes HIV that causes AIDS?
   A. contain highly porous plasma membranes
   B. has RNA instead of DNA
   C. made of cells without nuclei
   D. use their DNA to replicate host DNA

Part B: Matching and Completion

Matching *Write the letter of the correct archaebacteria on the line next to its description. Answers may be used only once or not at all.*

_____ 1. live in deep ocean thermal vents

_____ 2. tolerate high salt concentrations

_____ 3. located in human digestive systems

A. halophiles

B. methanogens

C. thermoacidophiles

D. cyanobacteria

Copyright © Glencoe/McGraw-Hill, a division of The McGraw-Hill Companies, Inc.

Chapter Test B CONTINUED

Completion *Write the correct term in the blank to complete each sentence below.*

4. Unlike eukaryotes, prokaryotic cells do not store genetic information inside

   a(n) _____ .

5. A spherically shaped bacterium is called a(n) _____ .

6. Prokaryotes with a rod shape are called _____ .

7. Bacteria breaking down a dead tree into nutrient-rich soil are acting

   as _____ .

8. A strand of genetic material surrounded by a protein coat is called

   a(n) _____ .

9. An infectious particle made entirely of protein is called a(n) _____ .

Part C: Interpreting Drawings

*Use **Figure 1** to respond to each statement.*

1. **Identify** the type of cell represented by **Figure 1.**

   _____

2. **Identify** the cell parts labeled *A*, *B*, *C*, and *D*.

   A. _____

   B. _____

   C. _____

   D. _____

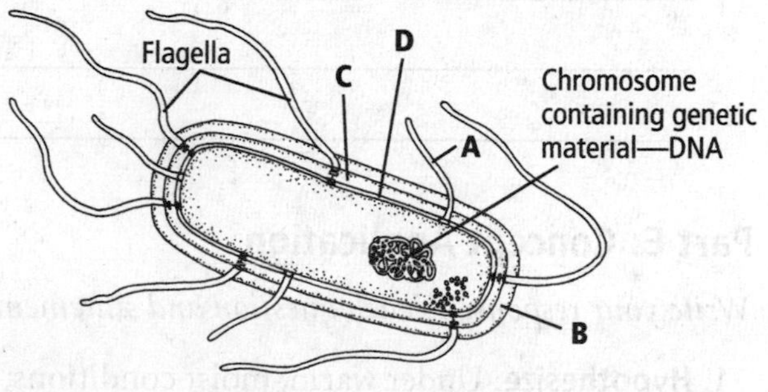

Flagella C D Chromosome containing genetic material—DNA A B

Figure 1

*Use **Figure 2** to respond to each statement.*

3. **Identify** the structure represented by **Figure 2.**

   _____

4. **Identify** the parts labeled *A* and *B*.

   A. _____

   B. _____

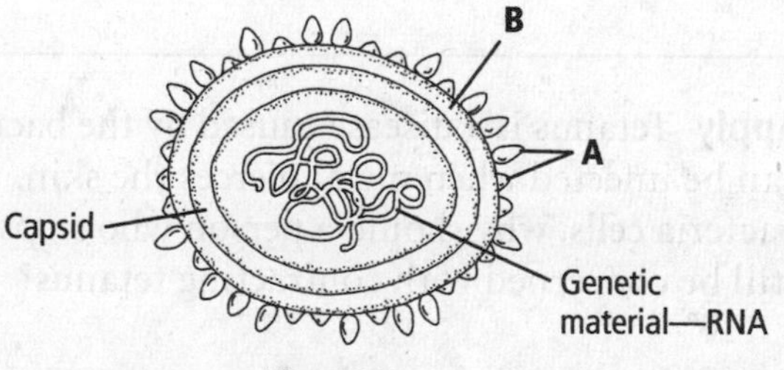

B A Capsid Genetic material—RNA

Figure 2

Copyright © Glencoe/McGraw-Hill, a division of The McGraw-Hill Companies, Inc.

Chapter Test B CONTINUED

Part D: Short Answer

Write your response to each statement in the space provided.

1. **Explain** why a doctor would order a Gram stain on a bacteria sample taken from an infected patient.

   _____

   _____

   _____

2. **Infer** why humans would not be able to repair and grow muscle without bacteria.

   _____

   _____

   _____

3. **Contrast** chemoautotrophs and photoautotrophs.

   _____

   _____

   _____

Part E: Concept Application

Write your response to each question and statement in the space provided.

1. **Hypothesize** Under warm, moist conditions, bacteria can reproduce every 20 min. Write a hypothesis about how the rate of binary fission can create a health crisis.

   _____

   _____

   _____

2. **Apply** Tetanus is a disease caused by the bacteria *Clostridium tetani,* and a person can be infected when metal pierces the skin. If extreme heat and dry conditions kill bacteria cells, why should a person who steps on a nail while walking in a hot desert still be concerned with contracting tetanus?

   _____

   _____

   _____

Copyright © Glencoe/McGraw-Hill, a division of The McGraw-Hill Companies, Inc.

Chapter Test **C**

CHAPTER 18
Bacteria and Viruses

Part A: Multiple Choice

In the space at the left, write the letter of the term or phrase that best completes each statement or answers each question.

_____ 1. Which is the result of conjugation?
   A. endospore creation
   B. genetic diversity
   C. nucleoid break down
   D. rapid cell reproduction

_____ 2. Without an endospore, a *Clostridium tetani* bacterium would not be able to _____
   A. complete binary fission.
   B. maintain genetic diversity.
   C. repair plasma membrane.
   D. survive extreme coldness.

_____ 3. *Escherichia coli* bacteria living in the human intestines manufacture _____
   A. fat.
   B. protein.
   C. vitamin D.
   D. vitamin K.

_____ 4. Which is a disease caused by bacteria?
   A. cold
   B. measles
   C. pneumonia
   D. rabies

_____ 5. Which is a stage of a host-cell infection by a virus?
   A. adaptation of viral receptors to infect most organism cells
   B. replication of viral DNA using host mitochondria DNA
   C. viral genetic material injected into the host cell's cytoplasm
   D. virus attaches to host cell membrane using a capsule

_____ 6. Which describes a retrovirus?
   A. enzyme-coated virus
   B. protein-coated virus
   C. virus with DNA
   D. virus with RNA

Part B: Completion

Write the correct term in the blank to complete each sentence below.

1. Organisms without a nucleus are called _____ .

2. Nutrients and other substances are moved throughout the body of a prokaryote by the process

   of _____ .

Copyright © Glencoe/McGraw-Hill, a division of The McGraw-Hill Companies, Inc.

Chapter Test C CONTINUED

3. Harmless prokaryotes living on human skin are called _____ .

4. The resistance of many bacteria strains to the antibiotic penicillin is a result

of _____ .

5. Viral DNA is integrated with the genetic material of a host cell during

the _____ .

6. An infectious, protein substance is called a(n) _____ .

Part C: Interpreting Drawings

*Use **Figure 1** to respond to each statement.*

1. Identify the type of cell represented by **Figure 1.**

_____

2. Identify the cell parts labeled *A–E.*

A. _____

B. _____

C. _____

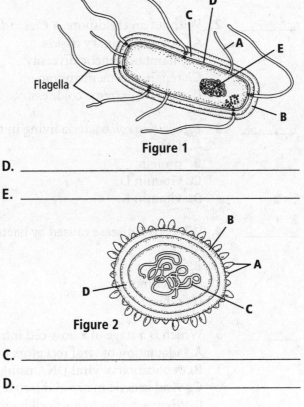

Flagella

Figure 1

D. _____

E. _____

*Use **Figure 2** to respond to each statement.*

3. Identify the structure represented by **Figure 2.**

_____

4. Identify the parts labeled *A–D.*

A. _____

B. _____

C. _____

D. _____

Figure 2

Part D: Short Answer

Write your response to each statement in the space provided.

1. Describe the variety of habitats of archaebacteria.

_____

_____

_____

Copyright © Glencoe/McGraw-Hill, a division of The McGraw-Hill Companies, Inc.

Chapter Test C CONTINUED

2. Infer how herbivorous white-tailed deer living in a deciduous forest are dependent on bacteria for their food supply.

_____

_____

_____

3. Contrast the ways obligate aerobes, obligate anaerobes, and facultative anaerobes obtain energy.

_____

_____

_____

Part E: Concept Application

Write your response to each question and statement in the space provided.

1. Apply A doctor diagnoses a patient with a bacterial infection. Before prescribing an antibiotic, what test must be completed? Why must this test be completed?

_____

_____

_____

2. Infer why leftover foods such as cooked meat should be refrigerated immediately.

_____

_____

_____

3. Identify Most scientists do not consider viruses to be alive because they have no organelles, cannot move, and cannot reproduce on their own. Identify other reasons why viruses are not considered living things.

_____

_____

_____

Copyright © Glencoe/McGraw-Hill, a division of The McGraw-Hill Companies, Inc.

CHAPTER 18
Assessment | **Student Recording Sheet**

Section 18.1

Vocabulary Review

Choose the vocabulary term that does not belong, and explain why it does not belong.

1. _____
   _____

2. _____
   _____

3. _____
   _____

Understand Key Concepts

Select the best answer from the choices given, and fill in the corresponding circle.

4. Ⓐ Ⓑ Ⓒ Ⓓ   6. Ⓐ Ⓑ Ⓒ Ⓓ   8. Ⓐ Ⓑ Ⓒ Ⓓ   10. Ⓐ Ⓑ Ⓒ Ⓓ

5. Ⓐ Ⓑ Ⓒ Ⓓ   7. Ⓐ Ⓑ Ⓒ Ⓓ   9. Ⓐ Ⓑ Ⓒ Ⓓ

Constructed Response

11. _____
    _____
    _____
    _____

12. _____
    _____
    _____

13. _____
    _____
    _____
    _____

Think Critically

14. _____
    _____

Copyright © Glencoe/McGraw-Hill, a division of The McGraw-Hill Companies, Inc.

CHAPTER 18
Assessment   Student Recording Sheet

15. _____

_____

16. _____

_____

Section 18.2

Vocabulary Review

Write a sentence that connects the vocabulary terms in each pair.

17. _____

_____

18. _____

_____

19. _____

_____

20. _____

_____

Understand Key Concepts

Select the best answer from the choices given, and fill in the corresponding circle.

21. Ⓐ Ⓑ Ⓒ Ⓓ   **23.** Ⓐ Ⓑ Ⓒ Ⓓ   **25.** Ⓐ Ⓑ Ⓒ Ⓓ   **27.** Ⓐ Ⓑ Ⓒ Ⓓ

22. Ⓐ Ⓑ Ⓒ Ⓓ   **24.** Ⓐ Ⓑ Ⓒ Ⓓ   **26.** Ⓐ Ⓑ Ⓒ Ⓓ

Constructed Response

28. _____

_____

_____

29. _____

_____

30. Record your answer for question 30 on a separate sheet of paper.

Copyright © Glencoe/McGraw-Hill, a division of The McGraw-Hill Companies, Inc.

CHAPTER 18
Assessment

Student Recording Sheet

Think Critically

31. _____
_____

32. _____
_____

33. _____
_____

34. _____
_____

Additional Assessment

35. **Writing in Biology** Record your answer for question 35 on a separate sheet of paper.

36. **Writing in Biology** _____
_____

Document-Based Questions

37. _____

38. _____
_____

39. _____
_____

Cumulative Review

40. _____
_____

41. _____
_____

42. _____
_____

43. _____
_____

Copyright © Glencoe/McGraw-Hill, a division of The McGraw-Hill Companies, Inc.

CHAPTER 18
Assessment | Student Recording Sheet

Standardized Test Practice

Multiple Choice

Select the best answer from the choices given, and fill in the corresponding circle.

1. Ⓐ Ⓑ Ⓒ Ⓓ   4. Ⓐ Ⓑ Ⓒ Ⓓ   7. Ⓐ Ⓑ Ⓒ Ⓓ
2. Ⓐ Ⓑ Ⓒ Ⓓ   5. Ⓐ Ⓑ Ⓒ Ⓓ   8. Ⓐ Ⓑ Ⓒ Ⓓ
3. Ⓐ Ⓑ Ⓒ Ⓓ   6. Ⓐ Ⓑ Ⓒ Ⓓ   9. Ⓐ Ⓑ Ⓒ Ⓓ

Short Answer

Answer each question with complete sentences.

10. _____

11. _____
    _____

12. _____
    _____

13. _____
    _____

14. _____

15. _____

Extended Response

Answer each question with complete sentences.

16. _____
    _____

17. _____
    _____

18. _____
    _____

19. _____
    _____

Essay Question

20. Record your answer for question 20 on a separate sheet of paper.

Copyright © Glencoe/McGraw-Hill, a division of The McGraw-Hill Companies, Inc.

Table of Contents

Chapter 19 Protists

Copyright © Glencoe/McGraw-Hill, a division of The McGraw-Hill Companies, Inc.

Diagnostic Test

CHAPTER 19
Protists

Before reading Chapter 19, predict answers to questions about the chapter content based on what you already know. Circle the letter of the correct answer, and then explain your reasoning.

1. A biologist is studying the organisms found in a drop of pond water. He views long strands of green algae and the roots of water hyacinth plants under the microscope's magnification. Swimming between the algae strands, he views amoebas, paramecium, and other protozoans. He also discovers microscopic aquatic worms thrashing in the water droplet as well as rotifers feeding around detritus. Which plantlike protist did the scientist observe?

   A. algae

   B. amoeba

   C. hyacinth

   D. rotifer

   Explain.

   _____

   _____

   _____

2. A hiker walks through a forest after a heavy rain. She lifts up a rotting log and discovers a bright yellow slime mold covering a portion of the wet wood. In a large puddle, she sees the fuzzy white strands of a water mold covering a dead insect. Which type of organism are the slime mold and water mold?

   A. algae

   B. fungi

   C. plant

   D. protist

   Explain.

   _____

   _____

   _____

3. A friend of yours describes small protists she saw under a microscope during a science lab. She believes all protists live in freshwater. Critique her hypothesis.

   _____

   _____

   _____

Copyright © Glencoe/McGraw-Hill, a division of The McGraw-Hill Companies, Inc.

Launch Lab

CHAPTER 19
What is a protist?

The Kingdom Protista is similar to a drawer or closet in which you keep odds and ends that do not seem to fit any other place. The Kingdom Protista is composed of three groups of organisms that do not fit in any other kingdom. In this lab, you will observe the three groups of protists.

Procedure 🥽 👔 🧤 🚫 ✋

1. Read and complete the lab safety form.
2. In the space below, construct a data table to record your observations.
3. Observe **different types of protists** using a **microscope,** noting their similarities and differences. Record your observations, notes, and illustrations in your data table.

Data and Observations

Analysis

1. **Organize** the protists with similar characteristics into groups using the data that you collected.

_____

_____

_____

2. **Infer** which of your groups are animal-like, plantlike, or funguslike.

_____

_____

Copyright © Glencoe/McGraw-Hill, a division of The McGraw-Hill Companies, Inc.

MiniLab

CHAPTER 19
Investigate Photosynthesis in Algae

How much sunlight does green algae need to undergo photosynthesis? Algae contain photosynthetic pigments that allow them to produce food by using energy from the Sun. Observe green algae to determine whether the amount of light affects photosynthesis.

Procedure 🥽 👔 🚫 ☣ 🧤

1. Read and complete the lab safety form.
2. Obtain samples of **green algae** from your teacher. Place the sample of each type of algae in different locations in the classroom. Be sure one location is completely dark.

3. Hypothesize what will happen to the algae in each location.
4. Check each specimen every other day for a week. Create a data table in the space below and record your observations.

Data and Observations

Analysis

1. **Describe** the evidence you used to determine whether photosynthesis was occurring.

_____

_____

_____

2. **Conclude** Was your hypothesis supported? Explain.

_____

_____

3. **Predict** What organelles would you expect to see if you looked at each type of algae under a microscope?

_____

Copyright © Glencoe/McGraw-Hill, a division of The McGraw-Hill Companies, Inc.

MiniLab

CHAPTER 19
Investigate Slime Molds

What is a slime mold? In a kingdom of interesting creatures, slime molds are perhaps the most interesting. Observe different types of slime molds, and observe the unusual nature of their "bodies."

Procedure 🌀 🧤 ☣ 🚫 🖐

1. Read and complete the lab safety form.
2. Obtain **slides of different specimens of slime molds.** Examine the slides under a **microscope.**

3. In the space below, create a data table to record your information. Sketch and describe each specimen.

Data and Observations

Analysis

1. **Compare** and **contrast** the specimens.

_____

_____

_____

2. **Identify** specimens that have similar characteristics. Explain why the specimens are similar.

_____

_____

3. **Think Critically** How would you classify each specimen that you examined? Explain.

_____

_____

_____

_____

Copyright © Glencoe/McGraw-Hill, a division of The McGraw-Hill Companies, Inc.

Design Your Own
BioLab

CHAPTER 19
Investigate: How do protozoa behave?

Background: Animals respond and react to the world around them. One such type of reaction is known as *taxis* in which an animal orients itself toward (positive) or away (negative) from a stimulus. Some of the things animals respond to are light (photo-taxis), temperature (thermotaxis), chemicals (chemotaxis), and gravity (gravitaxis).

Question: *How do simple unicellular, animal-like protozoa respond to stimuli?*

Materials
cultures of live protozoa
compound microscope
glass slides and cover slips
materials needed to produce stimuli

Safety Precautions 🥽 👕 🧤 ☣ 🚫 ✋

WARNING: *Use care when handling slides. Dispose of any broken glass in a container provided by your teacher. Always wear goggles in the lab.*

Plan and Perform the Experiment
1. Read and complete the lab safety form.
2. Design an experiment to answer the question. Reword the original question to include the taxis you plan to investigate.

3. When complete, have your teacher approve your experimental design.
4. Collect the materials and supplies needed and begin conducting your experiment.
5. Dispose of your protozoan cultures as instructed by your teacher.

Data and Observations

Copyright © Glencoe/McGraw-Hill, a division of The McGraw-Hill Companies, Inc.

Analyze and Conclude

1. **Observe and Infer** Some protozoa are often described as animal-like. What animal-like characteristics did you observe?

_____

_____

2. **State the Problem** What stimuli were you trying to test with your experimental design?

_____

3. **Hypothesize** What was your hypothesis for the question to be solved?

_____

4. **Summarize** What data did you collect during the experiment?

_____

_____

5. **Analyze and Conclude** Did your data support your hypothesis? What is your conclusion?

_____

_____

_____

6. **Error Analysis** Compare your data and conclusions with other students in your class. Explain the differences in data.

_____

_____

_____

Copyright © Glencoe/McGraw-Hill, a division of The McGraw-Hill Companies, Inc.

Real-World Biology: Analysis

CHAPTER 19
Algae in Your Foods

Marine animals depend on diatoms and other uni-cellular algae as their food source. Can you imagine eating crunchy diatoms for lunch? People have been eating many species of multicellular algae since ancient times. They are good sources of many different vitamins and minerals.

Although algae are not plants, the algae that people eat are often called seaweed. People in Japan, Scotland, Norway, the Pacific Islands, coastal South American countries, and other countries near coastal water have eaten seaweed for thousands of years. Today, algae are harvested, dried, and shipped around the world.

Because algae can be shipped anywhere, people in countries far from coastal water can prepare foods with algae.

People boil algae as vegetables, use them in soups and as seasoning in rice dishes, use them as snack food, and cook them with soybeans. Most algae eaten by people are red and brown algae, but some green algae also are eaten. **Table 1** lists a few of the many species of algae commonly used today. Have you ever eaten algae? If you answered no, you might be surprised. In this activity, you will investigate food additives made from algae.

Table 1

Algae	Product	Foods
Brown algae: many species of *Laminaria*, such as *Laminaria angustata* and *Laminaria longissima*	usually sold dried and known as kombu	used to season broth and soup; deep-fried or sautéed; used as an ingredient in main dishes
Brown algae: *Undaria pinnatifida*	usually sold dried, but sometimes available raw and known as wakame	softened by soaking in water and used in soups and salads
Red algae: many species of *Porphyra*, such as *Porphyra tenera*	usually sold as dry sheets known as nori or laver	toasted and used to wrap sushi, rice balls, or rice crackers; crumbled and sprinkled on foods such as rice and noodles

Laminaria angustata   *Laminaria longissima*   *Porphyra tenera*

Algae and Food Additives

If you eat mostly fresh fruits and vegetables, grains, and unprocessed foods, you don't eat many food additives. However, stores are filled with processed and packaged foods that make preparing and eating meals easier. Food additives make the preparation of these foods possible, make them taste and look better, and keep them fresh and safe to eat. Three food additives that are made from algae are listed in **Table 2.** Some common foods that often contain these additives are listed in **Table 3.** Study the tables, and then answer the questions.

Copyright © Glencoe/McGraw-Hill, a division of The McGraw-Hill Companies, Inc.

Table 2

Food Additive	Sources	Uses
Agar	red algae, such as *Gelidium*, *Gracilaria*, and *Pterocladia*	used for thickening and suspending; used for stabilizing, to help foods maintain a uniform texture or consistency; used as a substitute for gelatin; used as an anti-drying agent in breads and pastry
Alginates	brown algae, such as *Macrocystis* and *Laminaria*	used for thickening, suspending, emulsifying, gel forming, and film forming; used for stabilizing, to help foods maintain a uniform texture or consistency
Carrageenan	red algae, such as *Gigartina stellata*, *Chondrus crispus*, and *Eucheuma*	used as a thickener; used for stabilizing, to help foods maintain a uniform texture or consistency

Table 3

Food	Agar	Alginates	Carrageenan
Bread			X
Cheese	X		X
Chocolate milk			X
Creamed soup			X
Dairy dessert			X
Dry mix		X	
Evaporated milk			X
Frozen food	X	X	X
Fruit juice	X	X	X
Ice cream		X	X
Milk pudding		X	X
Pasta			X
Sauce and gravy		X	X
Syrup, topping, and icing		X	
Whipped topping		X	X
Yogurt	X		X

Analyze and Conclude

Respond to each question and statement.

1. **Name** some foods or food additives made from algae.

2. **List** the genera of algae that are used most often as foods.

3. **Apply** Gelatin is an animal product used to make jelly-like desserts. Using your knowledge of food additives, tell what a vegetarian could use to make jelly-like desserts.

4. **Infer** Using your knowledge of algae and geography, why do you think algae are eaten more often in Japan and Pacific Ocean islands than in Arizona and New Mexico?

5. **Judge** Why might it be desirable to make food additives from algae?

CAREERS IN BIOLOGY

Food Technology Visit biologygmh.com for information on food technologists. What are the responsibilities of a food technologist?

 Copyright © Glencoe/McGraw-Hill, a division of The McGraw-Hill Companies, Inc.

Enrichment

Group Project: Impact of Protists on Humans

Protists are some of the most diverse organisms on Earth. They include unicellular, multicellular, and colonial organisms and can be similar to animals, plants, and fungi. Protists obtain nutrients through photosynthesis and also by ingesting other organisms, scavenging dead plant or animal debris, and living within other organisms as parasites. Some protists have major impacts on humans, causing human disease and destroying crops.

Select Working in a small group, select one of the protist species listed in the table to research in depth. For example, one group in your class might choose to research *Plasmopara viticola*, while another group researches *Trypanosoma brucei*.

Research Once you have selected a protist, find out how humans are currently affected by the organism or have been affected by the organism in the past. Use your textbook and other reference books to find the information. Look for photographs of the protist.

Your research should include eradication methods that have been used or are being used. Also find information about the protist's habitat, life cycle, and method of disease transmission.

Present Finally, present the information that you learned about the protist to your class. Display any photographs of the protist that you found. A diagram showing the protist's life cycle, including any host organisms, would be useful.

Type of Protist	Protist Species Name	Impact on Humans
Protozoa—animal-like	*Cryptosporidium parvum*	human intestinal problems
	Giardia lamblia	human intestinal problems
	Trypanosoma brucei	African sleeping sickness
	Trypanosoma cruzi	Chagas' disease
Algae—plantlike	*Gymnodinium catenatum*	red tides, toxic to humans
	Pfiesteria piscicida	human neurological or skin disorders
Funguslike	*Phytophthora infestans*	Irish potato blight
	Plasmopara viticola	downy mildew of grapes

Copyright © Glencoe/McGraw-Hill, a division of The McGraw-Hill Companies, Inc.

Concept
Mapping

The Classification of Protists

Complete the network tree about the classification of protists. These terms may be used more than once: algae, cilia, ciliates, flagella, food, nutrients, protists, protozoans, pseudopods, slime molds, sporozoans.

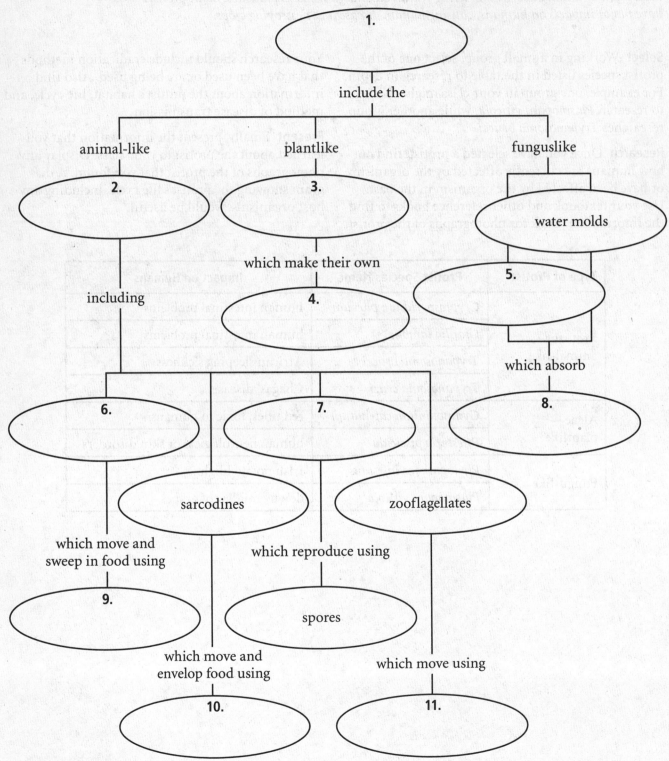

Copyright © Glencoe/McGraw-Hill, a division of The McGraw-Hill Companies, Inc.

Study Guide

CHAPTER 19
Section 1: Introduction to Protists

In your textbook, read about protists.

Match the definition in Column A with the term in Column B.

Column A		Column B
_____	1. protist that makes its own food through photosynthesis	**A.** eukaryotic
_____	2. protist that eats other unicellular organisms	**B.** microsporidium
_____	3. protist that absorbs its nutrients from dead organisms	**C.** water mold
_____	4. type of cell that all protists have	**D.** protozoan
_____	5. digests wood for termites	**E.** alga

In your textbook, read about classifying protists and the origin of protists.

Use each of the terms below only once to complete the passage.

amoeba	autotroph	endosymbiosis	evolutionary history
food	food source	heterotroph	kelp

The classification of protists into three groups is based on their **(6)** _____ .

For example, the diagram above shows a(n) **(7)** _____ . It is shown eating

(8) _____ , which makes it a(n) **(9)** _____ .

The giant **(10)** _____ , which is a(n) **(11)** _____ ,

is an example of a plantlike protist. The **(12)** _____ of protists is not well

known. However, **(13)** _____ is thought to have been part of this process.

Copyright © Glencoe/McGraw-Hill, a division of The McGraw-Hill Companies, Inc.

Study Guide

CHAPTER 19
Section 2: Protozoans—Animal-like Protists

In your textbook, read about paramecia.

Label the diagram of the paramecium. Use these choices:

    cilia   **contractile vacuole**   **macronucleus**   **micronucleus**   **oral groove**

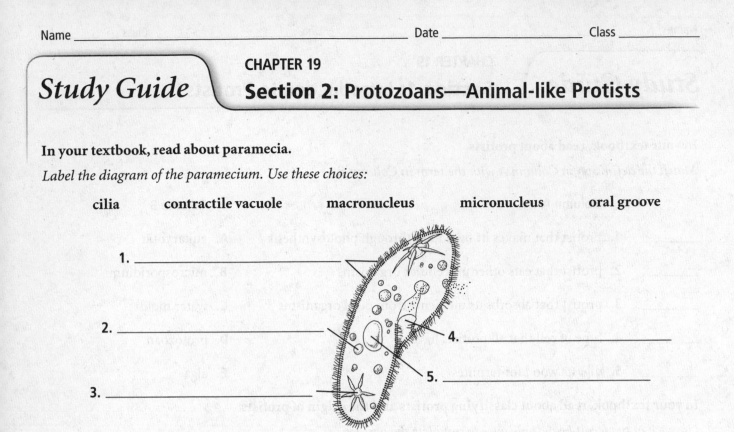

1. _____

2. _____

3. _____

4. _____

5. _____

In your textbook, read about Ciliophora, Sarcodina, Apicomplexa, and Zoomastigina.

Complete the table by checking the correct column(s) for each description.

Description	Ciliophora	Sarcodina	Apicomplexa	Zoomastigina
6. Reproduce through spores				
7. Use flagella for movement				
8. Have numerous short, hairlike projections				
9. Use pseudopods for feeding and locomotion				

Respond to each statement.

10. Name two phyla of protists that have members that cause diseases in humans.

_____

_____

11. Describe what Chagas' disease is and what causes it.

_____

_____

12. Explain how African sleeping sickness is transmitted to humans.

_____

_____

_____

Copyright © Glencoe/McGraw-Hill, a division of The McGraw-Hill Companies, Inc.

Study Guide

CHAPTER 19

Section 3: Algae—Plantlike Protists

In your textbook, read about the characteristics, diversity, and life cycle of algae.

If the statement is true, write true. *If the statement is false, replace the italicized term or phrase to make it true.*

1. The three criteria used to classify algae are the types of chlorophyll and secondary pigments, the method of *chlorophyll* storage, and the composition of the cell wall.

_____

2. All algae are considered *plantlike* because they contain photosynthetic pigments.

_____

3. Algal blooms occur when *euglenoids* reproduce in great numbers due to plentiful food and favorable environmental conditions.

_____

4. *Bioluminescent* dinoflagellates emit light and are usually found in salt water.

_____

5. Algae that have characteristics of both plants and animals are *chrysophytes*.

_____

6. The secondary pigment fucoxanthin accounts for the color of *red algae*.

_____

7. Algae are high in protein and contain *minerals, trace elements, and vitamins*.

_____

8. Many algae have a life cycle called *alternation of generations*.

_____

In your textbook, read about the life cycle of algae.

Label the diagram. Use these choices:

gametes   gametophytes   spores   sporophyte

9. _____

10. _____

11. _____

12. _____

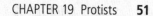

Copyright © Glencoe/McGraw-Hill, a division of The McGraw-Hill Companies, Inc.

Study Guide

Section 4: Funguslike Protists

In your textbook, read about funguslike protists.

Write the term or phrase that best completes each statement. Use these choices:

acrasin	**chitin**	**Myxomycota**
Oomycota	*Phytophthora infestans*	**plasmodium**

1. The cell walls of funguslike protists do not contain _____ like the cell

   walls of true fungi.

2. Some slime molds form a(n) _____ , which is a moving mass of cytoplasm.

3. A chemical called _____ signals slime mold amoeboid cells to congregate

   and form a single sluglike colony.

4. Acellular slime molds belong to the phylum _____ .

5. Water molds and downy mildew in the phylum _____ are often found

   in water or damp places.

6. The downy mildew _____ devastated the potato crop in Ireland in

   the nineteenth century, causing many people to starve.

In your textbook, read about slime molds.

Identify the following life cycles as cycles for acellular slime molds or cellular slime molds.

Haploid amoeba-like cells → sexual reproduction → diploid zygote → giant cell →
meiosis, then multiple mitosis → cell rupture → haploid amoeba-like cells

7. _____

Spores → haploid flagellated and amoeba-like cells → fertilization → diploid
plasmodium → meiosis → spores

8. _____

The diagram shows a multicellular amoeba-like mass.
For each statement below, write true *or* false.

9. The diagram shows a plasmodium.

   _____

10. The diagram shows a cellular slime mold.

   _____

Multicellular
amoeba-like mass

Copyright © Glencoe/McGraw-Hill, a division of The McGraw-Hill Companies, Inc.

Guía de estudio

En tu libro de texto, lee acerca de los protistas.

Relaciona la definición de la columna A con el término de la columna B.

Columna A

Columna B

_____ 1. protista que produce su propio alimento a través de la fotosíntesis

A. eucariota

_____ 2. protista que come otros organismos unicelulares

B. microsporidio

_____ 3. protista que absorbe sus nutrientes de organismos muertos

C. moho de agua

_____ 4. tipo de célula que todos los protistas tienen

D. protozoario

_____ 5. digiere madera para las termitas

E. alga

En tu libro de texto, lee acerca de la clasificación y el origen de los protistas.

Usa cada uno de los siguientes términos sólo una vez para completar el párrafo.

alimento	ameba	autótrofo	endosimbiosis
fuente alimenticia	heterótrofo	historia evolutiva	kelp

La clasificación de los protistas en tres grupos se basa en su **(6)** _____ . Por ejemplo, el diagrama anterior muestra una **(7)** _____ . Aparece absorbiendo **(8)** _____ , lo cual la hace un **(9)** _____ . El **(10)** _____ gigante, el cual es un **(11)** _____ , es un ejemplo de un protista tipo planta. La **(12)** _____ de los protistas no es muy conocida. Sin embargo, se considera que la **(13)** _____ ha sido parte de este proceso.

Copyright © Glencoe/McGraw-Hill, a division of The McGraw-Hill Companies, Inc.

Guía de estudio

En tu libro de texto, lee acerca de los paramecios.

Identifica el diagrama del paramecio. Usa estas opciones:

cilio   hendidura oral   macronúcleo   micronúcleo   vacuola contráctil

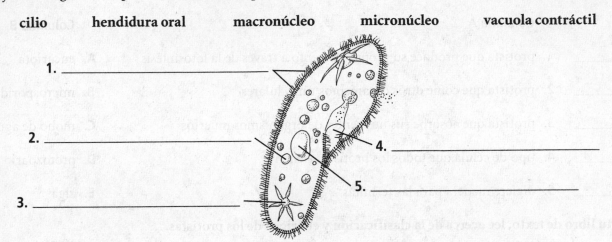

1. _____

2. _____

3. _____

4. _____

5. _____

En tu libro de texto, lee acerca de los Ciliados, Sarcodinos, Apicomplejos y Zoomastiginos.

Completa la tabla marcando la(s) columna(s) correcta(s) para cada descripción.

Descripción	Ciliados	Sarcodinos	Apicomplejos	Zoomastiginos
6. Se reproducen por medio de esporas				
7. Usan flagelos para el movimiento				
8. Tienen varias proyecciones cortas parecidas al pelo				
9. Usan seudópodos para alimentación y locomoción				

Responde a cada afirmación.

10. **Nombra** los dos filos de protistas que tienen miembros que provocan enfermedades en los humanos.

_____

_____

11. **Describe** qué es la enfermedad de Chagas y qué la provoca.

_____

_____

12. **Explica** cómo se transmite a los humanos la enfermedad africana del sueño.

_____

_____

Copyright © Glencoe/McGraw-Hill, a division of The McGraw-Hill Companies, Inc.

Guía de estudio

Sección 3: Algas—Protistas semejantes a las plantas

En tu libro de texto, lee acerca de las características, la diversidad y el ciclo de vida de las algas.

Si la afirmación es verdadera, escribe «verdadero». Si la afirmación es falsa, sustituye el término o la frase en cursiva para volverla verdadera.

1. Los tres criterios utilizados para clasificar las algas son los tipos de clorofila y pigmentos secundarios, el método de almacenamiento *de la clorofila* y la composición de la pared celular.

_____

2. Todas las algas se consideran *semejantes a las plantas* debido a que contienen pigmentos fotosintéticos.

_____

3. Los florecimientos algales ocurren cuando *los euglenoides* se reproducen en grandes cantidades debido a abundancia de alimento y a condiciones ambientales favorables.

_____

4. Los dinoflagelados *bioluminiscentes* emiten luces y por lo general se encuentran en el agua salada.

_____

5. Las algas que tienen características tanto de plantas como de animales son *crisófitas*.

_____

6. El pigmento secundario fucoxantina es el responsable del color del *alga roja*.

_____

7. Las algas tienen muchas proteínas y contienen *minerales, elementos traza y vitaminas*.

_____

8. Muchas algas tienen un ciclo de vida llamado *alternación de generaciones*.

_____

En tu libro de texto, lee acerca del ciclo de vida del alga.

Identifica el diagrama. Usa estas opciones:

esporas   esporofitos   gametos   gametofitos

9. _____

10. _____

11. _____

12. _____

Copyright © Glencoe/McGraw-Hill, a division of The McGraw-Hill Companies, Inc.

Guía de estudio

CAPÍTULO 19
Sección 4: Protistas semejantes a los hongos

En tu libro de texto, lee acerca de los protistas semejantes a los hongos.

Escribe el término que mejor completa cada afirmación. Usa estas opciones:

acrasina   Mixomicetes   Oomicetes
Phytophthora infestans   plasmodio   quitina

1. Las paredes celulares de los protistas semejantes a los hongos no contienen

   _____ como las paredes celulares de los hongos verdaderos.

2. Algunos mohos limosos forman un _____, el cual es una masa de

   citoplasma en movimiento.

3. Un químico llamado _____ indica a las células ameboides del moho

   limoso que se congreguen y formen una sola colonia semejante a la babosa.

4. Los mohos limosos acelulares pertenecen al filo _____ .

5. Los mohos de agua y el moho lanudo del filo _____ a menudo se

   encuentran en el agua o lugares húmedos.

6. El moho lanudo _____ acabó con la cosecha de papas en Irlanda en

   el siglo XIX, lo que provocó hambruna entre la gente.

En tu libro de texto, lee acerca de los mohos limosos.

Identifica los siguientes ciclos de vida como los ciclos de los mohos limosos acelulares o de los mohos limosos celulares.

Células haploides semejantes a la ameba → reproducción sexual → cigoto diploide →
célula gigante → meiosis, luego mitosis múltiple → ruptura celular → células haploides
semejantes a la ameba

7. _____

Esporas → células haploides flageladas y semejantes a la ameba → fertilización →
plasmodio diploide → meiosis → esporas

8. _____

*El diagrama muestra una masa multicelular semejante a la ameba. Para cada afirmación a
continuación, escribe «verdadero» o «falso».*

9. El diagrama muestra un plasmodio.

   _____

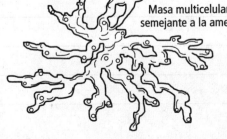

Masa multicelular
semejante a la ameba

10. El diagrama muestra un moho limoso celular.

    _____

Copyright © Glencoe/McGraw-Hill, a division of The McGraw-Hill Companies, Inc.

Section Quick Check

Section 1: Introduction to Protists

After reading the section in your textbook, respond to each statement.

1. Recall where protists are usually found.

_____

_____

2. Identify the characteristics an organism must have to be a member of Kingdom Protista.

_____

_____

3. Explain why the organization of Kingdom Protista will most likely change.

_____

_____

_____

4. Apply the theory of endosymbiosis to the existence of photosynthetic protists.

_____

_____

_____

_____

_____

5. Correct the following statement: Archaebacteria and certain of their organelles evolved from eubacteria and protists.

_____

_____

_____

_____

Copyright © Glencoe/McGraw-Hill, a division of The McGraw-Hill Companies, Inc.

After reading the section in your textbook, respond to each statement.

1. **Name** the characteristic of protozoans that biologists use for classification.

_____

_____

2. **Describe** the structure of an amoeba.

_____

_____

_____

_____

3. **Compare** and **contrast** the structure and function of cilia and flagella.

_____

_____

4. **Decide** whether sarcodines are more like ciliates or sporozoans. Explain.

_____

_____

_____

5. **Speculate** about whether or not a paramecium that lives in the ocean would need a contractile vacuole.

_____

_____

_____

_____

Copyright © Glencoe/McGraw-Hill, a division of The McGraw-Hill Companies, Inc.

Section Quick Check

Section 3: Algae—Plantlike Protists

After reading the section in your textbook, respond to each statement.

1. List the three characteristics scientists use to classify algae.

_____

_____

_____

2. Discuss the reasons that green algae are considered the algae most like plants.

_____

_____

_____

3. Summarize the process of alternation of generations, which occurs in the life cycles of many algae.

_____

_____

_____

_____

4. Differentiate the way in which diatoms store their food from the way in which other algae store food.

_____

_____

5. Assess the importance of algae to humans.

_____

_____

_____

_____

Copyright © Glencoe/McGraw-Hill, a division of The McGraw-Hill Companies, Inc.

Section
Quick Check

CHAPTER 19
Section 4: Funguslike Protists

After reading the section in your textbook, respond to each statement.

1. **State** where water molds and downy mildews live.

   _____

   _____

2. **Recount** how a downy mildew affected the population of the United States in the nineteenth century.

   _____

   _____

   _____

   _____

3. **Discuss** why slime molds in the phylum Myxomycota are called acellular.

   _____

   _____

   _____

   _____

4. **Compare** and **contrast** slime molds and fungi.

   _____

   _____

   _____

   _____

5. **Distinguish** the motile masses of acellular and cellular slime molds.

   _____

   _____

   _____

   _____

Copyright © Glencoe/McGraw-Hill, a division of The McGraw-Hill Companies, Inc.

Chapter Test **A**

CHAPTER 19
Protists

Part A: Multiple Choice

In the space at the left, write the letter of the term or phrase that best completes each statement or answers each question.

_____ **1.** Which do scientists use to classify protists into groups?
  A. features of their habitats
  B. methods of obtaining food
  C. organelles and other structures
  D. size and appearance

_____ **2.** A plantlike protist that has two flagella and is capable of bioluminescence is called a(n) _____
  A. chrysophyte.
  B. diatom.
  C. dinoflagellate.
  D. euglenoid.

_____ **3.** An intricately shaped plantlike protist consisting of two halves is called a(n) _____
  A. chrysophyte.
  B. diatom.
  C. dinoflagellate.
  D. euglenoid.

Part B: Matching

Matching Set 1 *Write the letter of the correct term on the line next to its description or members. Answers may be used only once.*

_____ **1.** have a whiplike projection called a flagella   **A.** Apicomplexa

_____ **2.** includes all species of amoebas   **B.** Ciliophora

_____ **3.** uses the sexual process called conjugation   **C.** Sarcodina

_____ **4.** contains parasitic sporozoans   **D.** Zoomastigina

Matching Set 2 *Write the letter of the correct plantlike protist group on the line next to its description or members. Answers may be used only once.*

_____ **5.** includes the most common species of algae found in   **A.** brown algae
             North American freshwater
                                                                         B. green algae
_____ **6.** used to thicken puddings, syrups, and shampoos
                                                                         C. red algae
_____ **7.** includes all species of kelp

Copyright © Glencoe/McGraw-Hill, a division of The McGraw-Hill Companies, Inc.

Chapter Test A CONTINUED

Part C: Interpreting Drawings and Graphs

Use Figure 1 to respond to the following statement.

1. Infer the phylum under which this protist would be classified. Explain.

_____

_____

_____

Use Figure 2 to respond to each statement.

2. Explain why the line labeled *chloroplasts* extends from the photosynthetic bacteria arrow to the photosynthetic protist arrow.

_____

_____

_____

_____

_____

3. Infer what the diagram illustrates about the evolutionary history of thermophiles.

_____

_____

_____

_____

_____

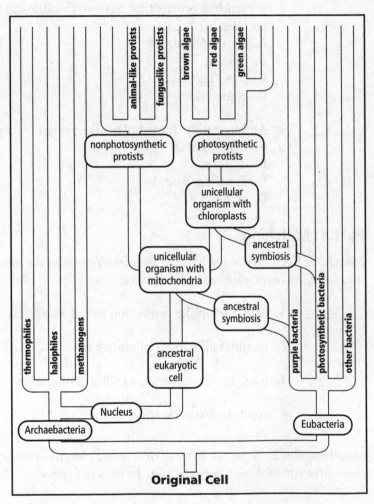

Figure 1

Figure 2

Copyright © Glencoe/McGraw-Hill, a division of The McGraw-Hill Companies, Inc.

Chapter Test A CONTINUED

Part D: Short Answer

Write your response to each statement in the space provided.

1. In a freshwater pond deep in the Amazon rain forest, a scientist discovers a new organism. **Identify** two characteristics she would use to classify the organism into Kingdom Protista.

_____

_____

_____

2. **Describe** the alternation of generations life cycle of the sea lettuce *Ulva*.

_____

_____

_____

Part E: Concept Application

Write your response to each statement in the space provided.

1. **Contrast** animal-like, plantlike, and funguslike protists. Include their method for obtaining nutrition and their capacity for movement.

_____

_____

_____

_____

_____

2. **Describe** If you are planning a hike through a forest and would like to observe slime molds, describe two habitats where you would search for these protists.

_____

_____

_____

_____

_____

Copyright © Glencoe/McGraw-Hill, a division of The McGraw-Hill Companies, Inc.

Name _____ Date _____ Class _____

Chapter Test **B**

CHAPTER 19
Protists

Part A: Multiple Choice

In the space at the left, write the letter of the phrase that best completes each statement or answers each question.

_____ 1. Which describes organisms in Kingdom Protista?
   A. eukaryotes that use similar reproductive methods
   B. eukaryotes with a diversity of reproductive methods
   C. prokaryotes that use similar reproductive methods
   D. prokaryotes with a diversity of reproductive methods

_____ 2. Microsporidia are microscopic protozoa that live _____
   A. in freshwater ponds.
   B. in the gut of termites.
   C. on ocean surfaces.
   D. on the skin of mammals.

_____ 3. Organelles called contractile vacuoles enable a paramecium to _____
   A. dissolve nutrients for energy.
   B. get rid of excess water and waste products.
   C. maintain a constant temperature.
   D. pump salt into their cytoplasm.

_____ 4. Which describes amoeba reproduction?
   A. asexual reproduction in which a parent cell divides in half
   B. asexual reproduction in which two parent cells exchange DNA
   C. sexual reproduction in which a parent cell divides in half
   D. sexual reproduction in which two parent cells exchange DNA

_____ 5. Algae differ from plants because they do **not** have _____
   A. chloroplasts, roots, and stems.
   B. leaves, pigments, and roots.
   C. leaves, roots, and stems.
   D. pigments, roots, and stems.

Part B: Matching and Completion

Matching *Write the letter of the correct animal-like protist phylum on the line next to its description. Answers may be used only once or not at all.*

_____ 1. have both macronucleus and micronucleus   **A.** Apicomplexa

_____ 2. use pseudopods to move and collect food   **B.** Ciliophora

_____ 3. reproduce using spores   **C.** Sarcodina

_____ 4. contains organisms that cause sleeping sickness **D.** Sporozoan

                                                              E. Zoomastigina

Copyright © Glencoe/McGraw-Hill, a division of The McGraw-Hill Companies, Inc.

Chapter Test B CONTINUED

Completion *Write the term or phrase that best completes each statement.*

5. Protists that have both plant and animal characteristics are classified in phylum

   _____ .

6. Protists that bloom and turn ocean water red in color are called _____ .

7. Most freshwater algae species such as spirogyra are classified in phylum _____ .

8. Phylum Phaeophyta classifies kelp and other protists called _____ .

9. Algae in phylum Bacillariophyta that have two halves and display a wide variety of geometric shapes

   are called _____ .

10. Protists in phylum Rhodophyta that contain calcium carbonate

    and contribute to the formation of coral reefs are

    called _____ .

Part C: Interpreting Drawings and Graphs

*Use **Figure 1** to respond to the following statement.*

1. Study the drawing of the protist. **Infer** the phylum this protist would be
   classified under. Explain.

   _____

   _____

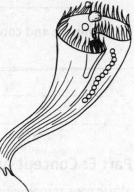

Figure 1

*Use **Figure 2** to respond to the following statements.*

2. **Compare** and **contrast** the major evolutionary
   advancements of nonphotosynthesizing protists
   with photosynthesizing protists.

   _____

   _____

   _____

   _____

3. **Predict** how the evolutionary history of protists might
   have been different if an ancestral eukaryotic cell had
   entered a symbiotic relationship with photosynthesizing
   bacteria instead of purple bacteria.

   _____

   _____

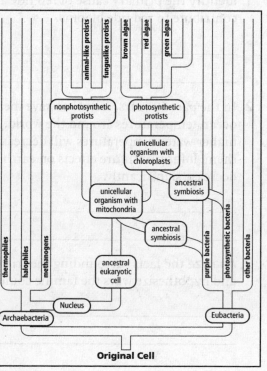

Figure 2

Copyright © Glencoe/McGraw-Hill, a division of The McGraw-Hill Companies, Inc.

Chapter Test B CONTINUED

Part D: Short Answer

Write your response to each statement in the space provided.

1. **Compare** and **contrast** the sexual processes and reproductive strategies of ciliates and sporozoans.

_____

_____

_____

2. **Describe** the alternation of generations life cycle of the sea lettuce *Ulva*.

_____

_____

_____

3. **Compare** and **contrast** slime molds and fungi.

_____

_____

_____

_____

Part E: Concept Application

Write your response to each statement in the space provided.

1. **Identify** the primary cause of red tide and infer how human activities could contribute to red tide blooms.

_____

_____

2. In the past 50 years, scientists have measured a significant increase in average ocean temperatures around the world, and many biologists are concerned that higher water temperatures will decrease diatom populations and other protists like them. **Infer** two future effects on earth's ecosystems if ocean protist populations decrease significantly.

_____

_____

_____

3. **Analyze** the facts surrounding the Irish potato famine of the nineteenth century and hypothesize ways the famine could have been lessened or averted.

_____

_____

_____

Copyright © Glencoe/McGraw-Hill, a division of The McGraw-Hill Companies, Inc.

Chapter Test C

CHAPTER 19
Protists

Part A: Multiple Choice

In the space at the left, write the letter of the term or phrase that best completes each statement or answers each question.

_____ 1. The three major groups of protists are classified based on their methods for _____
   A. locomotion.
   B. obtaining nutrition.
   C. producing food.
   D. reproduction.

_____ 2. Which are protozoans?
   A. amoebas, apicomplexans, ciliates
   B. apicomplexans, dinoflagellates, euglenoids
   C. diatoms, euglenoids, zooflagellates
   D. euglenoids, dinoflagellates, diatoms

_____ 3. Without contractile vacuoles, a paramecium would be unable to _____
   A. break down food into nutrients.
   B. maintain an internal homeostasis.
   C. pump water in from its environment.
   D. repair internal damage to organelles.

_____ 4. Which phylum classifies all amoeba species?
   A. Apicomplexa
   B. Ciliophora
   C. Sarcodina
   D. Zoomastigina

_____ 5. Algae blooms and red tide are cause by protists from phylum _____
   A. Bacillariophyta.
   B. Chrysophyta.
   C. Euglenophyta.
   D. Pyrrophyta.

_____ 6. Which protist can reproduce using the process of fragmentation?
   A. *Amoeba proteus*
   B. *Paramecium caudatum*
   C. *Spirogyra*
   D. *Trypanosoma*

Part B: Completion

Write the term or phrase that best completes each statement.

1. Ciliates vary the composition of their DNA by using the process of _____ .

2. Sporozoans are classified in phylum _____ .

Copyright © Glencoe/McGraw-Hill, a division of The McGraw-Hill Companies, Inc.

Chapter Test C CONTINUED

3. Unicellular protists that have both animal and plant characteristics are classified in phylum

_____ .

4. The silica walls of diatom shells allow them to be used as a(n) _____ .

5. Unlike true fungi, fungi-like protists lack the substance called _____ .

6. Aquatic protists that envelop their food with a mass of threads to absorb nutrients are called

_____ .

Part C: Interpreting Drawings and Graphs

*Use **Figure 1** to respond to the following statement.*

1. Study the drawing of the protist. **Infer** the phylum this protist would
   be classified under. Explain.

   _____

   _____

   _____

Figure 1

*Use **Figure 2** to respond to each statement.*

2. **Infer** why scientists believe chloroplasts were
   assimilated by protists at a later time than mitochondria.

   _____

   _____

   _____

   _____

3. **Hypothesize** why scientists believe an ancestral
   eukaryotic cell entered into a symbiotic relationship with
   purple bacteria, which evolved into modern-day protists.

   _____

   _____

   _____

   _____

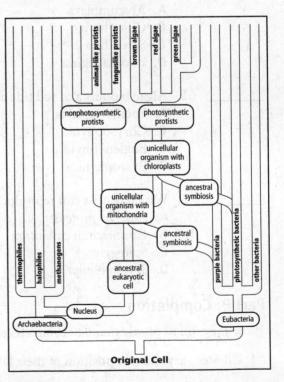

Figure 2

Copyright © Glencoe/McGraw-Hill, a division of The McGraw-Hill Companies, Inc.

Chapter Test C CONTINUED

Part D: Short Answer

Write your answer to each statement in the space provided.

1. Contrast how organisms from the three major groups of protists obtain nutrients.

_____

_____

_____

2. Describe the plasma membrane structure of a paramecium.

_____

_____

_____

3. Contrast the method of locomotion used by protists in phyla Ciliophora, Sarcodina, Apicomplexa, and Zoomastigina.

_____

_____

_____

4. Compare and **contrast** protists classified in phyla Chlorophyta, Phaeophyta, and Rhodophyta.

_____

_____

_____

Part E: Concept Application

Write your answer to each statement in the space provided.

1. Analyze the life cycle of protists from genus *Trypanosoma* and formulate several solutions for reducing the spread of African sleeping sickness.

_____

_____

_____

2. Infer the potential effect on the biosphere if environmental conditions suddenly prevented diatoms from storing their food as oil.

_____

_____

Copyright © Glencoe/McGraw-Hill, a division of The McGraw-Hill Companies, Inc.

CHAPTER 19
Assessment | Student Recording Sheet

Section 19.1

Vocabulary Review

Write complete sentences, using the vocabulary term that best answers each question.

1. _____

2. _____

Understand Key Concepts

Select the best answer from the choices given, and fill in the corresponding circle.

3. Ⓐ Ⓑ Ⓒ Ⓓ   5. Ⓐ Ⓑ Ⓒ Ⓓ   7. Ⓐ Ⓑ Ⓒ Ⓓ

4. Ⓐ Ⓑ Ⓒ Ⓓ   6. Ⓐ Ⓑ Ⓒ Ⓓ

Constructed Response

8. _____

_____

_____

9. **Careers in Biology** _____

_____

_____

Think Critically

10. _____

_____

_____

Section 19.2

Vocabulary Review

Write a definition for each structure, and provide an example of an organism where the structure could be found.

11. _____

_____

12. _____

_____

13. _____

_____

Copyright © Glencoe/McGraw-Hill, a division of The McGraw-Hill Companies, Inc.

CHAPTER 19
Assessment | **Student Recording Sheet**

Understand Key Concepts

Select the best answer from the choices given, and fill in the corresponding circle.

14. Ⓐ Ⓑ Ⓒ Ⓓ   15. Ⓐ Ⓑ Ⓒ Ⓓ   16. Ⓐ Ⓑ Ⓒ Ⓓ

Constructed Response

17. _____

_____

18. _____

_____

Think Critically

19.–20. Record your answers for questions 19 and 20 on a separate sheet of paper.

Section 19.3

Vocabulary Review

Write the vocabulary term that best matches each definition.

21. _____   22. _____   23. _____

Understand Key Concepts

Select the best answer from the choices given, and fill in the corresponding circle.

24. Ⓐ Ⓑ Ⓒ Ⓓ   26. Ⓐ Ⓑ Ⓒ Ⓓ   28. Ⓐ Ⓑ Ⓒ Ⓓ

25. Ⓐ Ⓑ Ⓒ Ⓓ   27. Ⓐ Ⓑ Ⓒ Ⓓ

Constructed Response

29. _____

_____

30. _____

_____

31. _____

_____

Think Critically

32. _____

_____

Copyright © Glencoe/McGraw-Hill, a division of The McGraw-Hill Companies, Inc.

CHAPTER 19
Assessment | Student Recording Sheet

33. _____

_____

Section 19.4

Vocabulary Review

Write the vocabulary term that makes each sentence true.

34. _____   **35.** _____

Understand Key Concepts

Select the best answer from the choices given, and fill in the corresponding circle.

36. Ⓐ Ⓑ Ⓒ Ⓓ   **37.** Ⓐ Ⓑ Ⓒ Ⓓ

Constructed Response

38. _____

_____

_____

39. Record your answer for question 39 on a separate sheet of paper.

Think Critically

40. _____

_____

Additional Assessment

41. Writing in Biology Record your answer for question 41 on a separate sheet of paper.

Document-Based Questions

42. _____

_____

43. _____

_____

44. _____

_____

Cumulative Review

45.–47. Record your answers for questions 45–47 on a separate sheet of paper.

Copyright © Glencoe/McGraw-Hill, a division of The McGraw-Hill Companies, Inc.

CHAPTER 19
Assessment Student Recording Sheet

Standardized Test Practice

Multiple Choice

Select the best answer from the choices given, and fill in the corresponding circle.

1. (A) (B) (C) (D)
2. (A) (B) (C) (D)
3. (A) (B) (C) (D)
4. (A) (B) (C) (D)

5. (A) (B) (C) (D)
6. (A) (B) (C) (D)
7. (A) (B) (C) (D)
8. (A) (B) (C) (D)

Short Answer

Answer each question with complete sentences.

9. Record your answer for question 9 on a separate sheet of paper.

10. _____
   _____
   _____

11. _____
   _____
   _____
   _____
   _____

12. _____
   _____
   _____

13. _____

Extended Response

Answer the following question with complete sentences.

14. _____
   _____
   _____
   _____

Essay Question

15. Record your answer for question 15 on a separate sheet of paper.

Copyright © Glencoe/McGraw-Hill, a division of The McGraw-Hill Companies, Inc.

Table of Contents

Chapter 20 Fungi

Copyright © Glencoe/McGraw-Hill, a division of The McGraw-Hill Companies, Inc.

Diagnostic Test

CHAPTER 20
Fungi

Before reading Chapter 20, predict answers to questions about the chapter content based on what you already know. Circle the letter of the correct answer, and then explain your reasoning.

1. A biology student is surveying forest floor organisms. She stops to observe the living things growing on a fallen log. She notices patches of dark moss and light green lichens growing on the log's surface. Green vines are wrapped around one end of the log, and brown mushrooms have sprouted from the log's moist underside. A black slime mold spreads out across the opposite side of the log. The student makes notes in her field journal. Which would be included in her notes?

   A. Forest floor plants growing on the log include moss, lichens, and vines.

   B. Mushroom roots extend across the log's surface and into decaying matter.

   C. The reproductive structures of mushroom fungi sprout in moist materials.

   D. Several species of fungi, including moss and slime mold, were observed.

   Explain.

   _____

   _____

   _____

2. Gerald discovers dozens of puffballs growing in his backyard after a night of rain. He squeezes a puffball, and a cloud of brown particles erupts from the sac. Gerald suspects that this is the way puffballs reproduce, and he decides to research fungi reproductive methods. Which would be part of his research?

   A. Fungi only use asexual reproduction to clone themselves.

   B. Fungi reproduce sexually to develop fungi seeds.

   C. Sperm cells are dispersed as a form of external fertilization.

   D. Spores are the primary reproductive structures of fungi.

   Explain.

   _____

   _____

   _____

3. A friend of yours is searching through her refrigerator when she discovers a half-filled jar of salsa covered with mold. In disgust, she claims that fungi serve no valuable purpose. Critique her statement, and discuss how you would respond to her.

   _____

   _____

   _____

Copyright © Glencoe/McGraw-Hill, a division of The McGraw-Hill Companies, Inc.

Launch Lab

CHAPTER 20
What differences exist among fungi?

Fungi display enormous diversity. The organisms in this kingdom vary in size from a single cell to a mushroom found in the Malheur National Forest that is 5.6 km wide! In this lab, you will observe some of the differences among fungi.

Procedure 🥽 🧤 🚫 🔥

1. Read and complete the lab safety form.
2. In the space below, create a data table to record your observations of the fungi samples provided by your teacher.
3. Study each fungus carefully. Wash your hands thoroughly after handling fungi.

4. Describe each fungus sample as completely as you can. Include properties like color, shape, size, and growth medium.
5. Dispose of fungi and clean your work station according to your teacher's instructions.

Data and Observations

Analysis

1. **Contrast** What physical characteristics varied most among your samples?

_____

_____

2. **Compare** Summarize any similarities you observed or can infer among the fungi you examined.

_____

_____

Copyright © Glencoe/McGraw-Hill, a division of The McGraw-Hill Companies, Inc.

MiniLab

CHAPTER 20
Examine Yeast Growth

What is the relationship between yeast reproduction and the availability of food?
Yeasts are unicellular fungi. These organisms feed on sugars, producing carbon dioxide
and ethyl alcohol in the process. Yeasts reproduce asexually and can multiply quickly
under optimal growth conditions.

Procedure 🥽 🧤 🚫 ☣ ✋

1. Read and complete the lab safety form.
2. Label four **250-mL Erlenmeyer flasks** 1–4.
3. In the space below, create a data table to record your results.
4. Add **100 mL warm water** to each flask and do not cover the flasks.
5. Add 0.0 g, 0.5 g, 1.0 g, or 1.5 g of **table sugar** to each one of the flasks.

6. Add one packet of **dry yeast** to each flask. Swirl flasks with a **glass rod** until contents are thoroughly mixed.
7. Observe and record the changes in the flasks every 5 min for 20 min.
8. Clean up your work station according to your teacher's instructions.

Data and Observations

Analysis

1. **Conclude** What is the relationship between yeast reproduction and the availability of sugar?

   _____

   _____

   _____

2. **Analyze** How might your results have changed if the flasks had been covered during your experiment?

   _____

   _____

   _____

Copyright © Glencoe/McGraw-Hill, a division of The McGraw-Hill Companies, Inc.

MiniLab

CHAPTER 20
Investigate Mold Growth

How does salt affect mold growth? Chemical preservatives, including salt (sodium chloride), are often used to influence mold growth on a variety of foods.

Procedure 🌊 👔 🧤

1. Read and complete the lab safety form.
2. Obtain two slices of **bread.** Touch one object in the room with both sides of both slices.
3. Using a **spray bottle** filled with **water,** lightly moisten both sides of both slices of bread evenly.
4. Place one bread slice into a **self-sealing bag.** Seal the bag and label it with your name, the date, and the object wiped with the bread.

5. Sprinkle **salt** on both sides of the second slice. Place the slice into another bag and seal it. Label this bag as you did the first, but note that salt was added.
6. In the space below, create a table to record your observations.
7. Record observations daily for ten days. Your table should include descriptions, as well as measurements of any mold that has formed.

Data and Observations

Analysis

1. **Identify** Which slice grew more mold?

_____

2. **Conclude** Did the salt affect mold growth?

_____

Copyright © Glencoe/McGraw-Hill, a division of The McGraw-Hill Companies, Inc.

Design Your Own
BioLab

How do environmental factors affect mold growth?

Background: Molds can grow under a wide range of conditions. Consider the differences in your kitchen alone. Molds can grow in a cool refrigerator or in a dark bread box on the counter. They grow on foods that contain varying amounts of sugar, protein, and moisture.

Question: *How does a specific environmental factor change the rate of mold growth?*

Materials
Choose materials that would be appropriate for this lab. Possible materials include:

mold from a food source
plain powdered gelatin (contains protein only)
bread
sugar

prepared gelatin in small cup
cotton swab
aluminum foil or plastic wrap
small cup
thermometer
graduated cylinder
spray bottle

Safety Precautions 🥽 🧤 ☣ 🚫 🖐

WARNING: *Never eat food used in the lab.*

Plan and Perform the Experiment

1. Read and complete the lab safety form.
2. Make a list of environmental factors that might affect mold growth. Based on this list, develop a question to investigate.
3. Design an experiment that will help you answer this question. Remember, only one environmental factor should vary in your experimental conditions.
4. Write your hypothesis and design a data table.

5. Make sure your teacher approves your plan before you proceed.
6. Use cotton swabs to transfer mold from the food source to your trial cups.
7. Record observations for 5–7 days.
8. **Cleanup and Disposal** Place trial cups in the area designated by your teacher. Clean and return all equipment used in the lab. Wash your hands thoroughly.

Data and Observations

Copyright © Glencoe/McGraw-Hill, a division of The McGraw-Hill Companies, Inc.

Analyze and Conclude

1. **Identify** What are the independent and dependent variables in your experiment?
Explain how the independent variable was changed.

_____

_____

_____

2. **Compare** Describe differences you noticed among trial samples.

_____

_____

3. **Describe** What steps did you take to limit variables in this experiment? Make a list
of constants.

_____

_____

_____

4. **Interpret the Data** How did the environmental factor you changed affect the rate of
mold growth?

_____

_____

5. **Conclude** Was your hypothesis supported? Explain.

_____

_____

_____

6. **Error Analysis** Is it possible that more than one variable was introduced in your
experiment? How would you change your experimental plans?

_____

_____

_____

Copyright © Glencoe/McGraw-Hill, a division of The McGraw-Hill Companies, Inc.

Real-World Biology: Lab

CHAPTER 20
Controlling Mold Growth

Mold spores move through the air outside and inside schools and homes. You can't see them, but tiny mold spores probably are floating past you in the air right now. When they land in a spot that provides the conditions they need to survive, they start to grow quickly. They get the nutrients they need by digesting and absorbing the material on which they are growing. The material could be carpet, walls, wood, paper, or even your food.

While some foods are made by using certain molds or fungi, most moldy foods should not be eaten. Such foods could possibly make you sick. Some scientists think certain mold spores and toxins produced by molds can make people sick if there are high concentrations in the air. People can reduce the chances of molds growing in their homes by controlling the conditions that molds need to grow. In this activity, you will investigate the conditions that affect the growth of mold and learn how mold growth can be controlled.

Procedure 🥽 🧤 🚯 ☣ ✋

1. Read and complete the lab safety form.

2. Obtain a **slice of white bread without preservatives** from your teacher, and let it stand uncovered overnight.

3. After 24 h, divide the slice of bread into four equal parts. Place them in **four clean petri dishes with lids** labeled as shown in the drawings below.

4. Use a **dropper** to add ten drops of **water** to the bread in dish B and ten drops of water to the bread in dish D.

5. Tape a lid on each of the four dishes. Place the petri dishes in a warm, dark closet or another dark area of the classroom.

6. Observe the petri dishes every day for the next several days. Record your observations in the table below. Look for signs of white, thready, or hairy growth. This is the common bread mold *Rhizopus*, a heterotrophic organism composed of many branching filaments called hyphae. Hyphae secrete an enzyme that digests organic substances to produce the characteristic "moldy" odor.

7. As soon as bread mold appears on one of your pieces of bread, place the petri dishes labeled "cold" (dishes C and D) in a dark container in the **refrigerator.** Be sure to mark the date in the table.

8. Compare the fungal growth among the petri dishes for the next several days. Record all your observations.

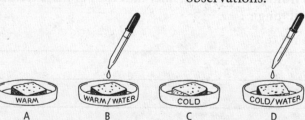

| | WARM | WARM / WATER | COLD | COLD/WATER |
| | A | B | C | D |

Observations (Presence of Mold, Color, and Other Characteristics)				
Date	Warm (A)	Warm/Water (B)	Cold (C)	Cold/Water (D)

Copyright © Glencoe/McGraw-Hill, a division of The McGraw-Hill Companies, Inc.

Analyze and Conclude

Respond to each question and statement.

1. **Identify** which petri dish showed the greatest mold growth.

   _____

2. **Explain** why bread mold might have failed to grow in a petri dish.

   _____

   _____

3. **Relate** Other than to dry out the bread, what was the purpose of leaving the bread out overnight in this experiment? By doing this, what do we learn about the reproductive strategies of fungi?

   _____

   _____

   _____

4. **Describe** how placing the petri dishes in a cold environment affected fungal growth.

   _____

   _____

   _____

5. **Discuss** Based on your observations, what would you do if you wanted to discourage the growth of mold?

   _____

   _____

6. People have developed a variety of methods, such as drying, canning, salting, and freezing, to prevent foods from decomposing. **Infer** how each of these techniques might inhibit the growth of fungi.

   _____

   _____

   _____

   _____

   _____

CAREERS IN BIOLOGY

Food Industry Visit biologygmh.com for information on food science technicians. What are the responsibilities of a food science technician?

Copyright © Glencoe/McGraw-Hill, a division of The McGraw-Hill Companies, Inc.

Enrichment

Analyze a Problem: Effects of Fungi

Fungi make up one of the most diverse groups of organisms on Earth. They are eukaryotes, and most are multicellular. Fungi form important symbiotic and mutualistic associations with other organisms. For example, most plants depend on fungi to assist in the absorption of minerals and nutrients from the soil. As decomposers, fungi play a vital role in terrestrial ecosystems. Fungi are important sources of food and drugs. However, they also can cause allergies, disease, and death. Fungi can be delicious or deadly.

Select Suppose you are writing an article about fungi for a scientific magazine. The table below lists seven species of fungi, the phylum to which each species belongs, uses of the fungi, and diseases and side effects caused by the fungi. Using the table, select one of the fungi to research.

Research Once you have selected a fungus, collect as much information as possible about it. Consider the following questions while researching the fungus: Does the fungus secrete any chemicals that make it useful or harmful to humans or other organisms? How, if at all, does the fungus cause disease?

Are there any historical examples of disease outbreaks or major problems caused by the fungus?

Discuss Use your textbook and other reference materials for information. Discuss your topic and possible answers to your questions with your teacher and classmates.

Write Finally, based on your research and class discussion, write an article about the fungus you selected. Provide answers for any questions you researched and discussed. Be sure to properly cite the sources you used to write your article.

Copyright © Glencoe/McGraw-Hill, a division of The McGraw-Hill Companies, Inc.

Fungi			
Species	**Phylum**	**Use**	**Disease/Toxicity**
Penicillium notatum	Deuteromycota (imperfect fungi)	source of antibiotic	
Claviceps purpurea	Ascomycota	treating high blood pressure, controlling bleeding	forms ergots on rye; if eaten, can cause gangrene, muscle pain, hallucinations, and death
Ophiostoma ulmi	Ascomycota		Dutch elm disease
Saccharomyces cerevisiae	Ascomycota	baking, brewing, and wine making	
Amanita phalloides	Basidiomycota		can cause death if eaten
Coccidioides immitis	Deuteromycota (imperfect fungi)		valley fever
Puccinia graminis	Basidiomycota		wheat rust

Concept Mapping

Feeding Relationships of Fungi

Complete the flowchart about feeding relationships of fungi. These terms may be used more than once: dead organisms, haustoria, living hosts, mutualistic, mutualistic relationship, other organisms, parasitic, raw materials, saprophytic, symbiotically, waste matter.

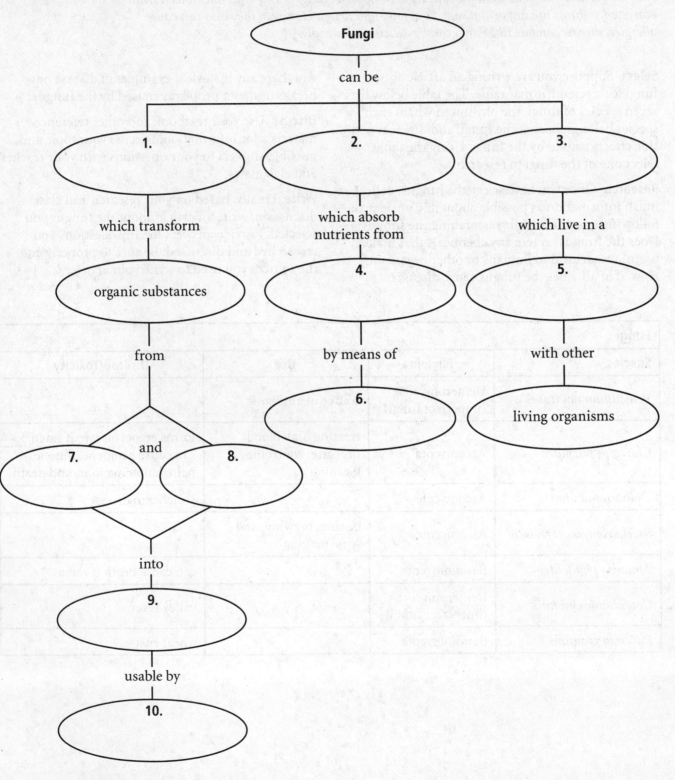

Copyright © Glencoe/McGraw-Hill, a division of The McGraw-Hill Companies, Inc.

Study Guide

In your textbook, read about the characteristics of fungi.

Match the definition in Column A with the term in Column B.

Column A		Column B
_____	1. netlike body of a fungus	**A.** fruiting body
_____	2. cross-walls between fungal cells	**B.** hyphae
_____	3. filaments in a multicellular fungus	**C.** mycelium
_____	4. unicellular fungus	**D.** septa
_____	5. fungal reproductive structure	**E.** yeast

In your textbook, read about nutrition in fungi.

Complete the table by checking the correct column(s) for each characteristic.

Fungi Characteristic	Saprophytic Fungi	Parasitic Fungi	Mutualistic Fungi
6. Harmful to host			
7. Helpful to host			
8. Heterotrophs			
9. Organic litter reducers			
10. Symbiosis			

In your textbook, read about reproduction in fungi.

Write the term that best completes each statement. Use these choices:

asexually	meiosis	sporangia	survival	wind

11. Fungi reproduce _____ by fragmentation, budding, or producing spores.

12. Producing a large number of spores increases a species' chances of _____ .

13. Fungal spores can be dispersed by animals, water, and _____ .

14. _____ protect spores and keep them from drying out until they are released.

15. Fungi might produce spores by _____ or mitosis.

Copyright © Glencoe/McGraw-Hill, a division of The McGraw-Hill Companies, Inc.

Study Guide

CHAPTER 20

Section 2: Diversity of Fungi

In your textbook, read about the diversity of fungi.

Match the definition in Column A with the term in Column B.

Column A

Column B

_____ 1. includes bread molds and other molds

A. Ascomycota

_____ 2. appears to lack a sexual stage in life cycle

B. Basidiomycota

_____ 3. produces flagellated spores

C. Chytridiomycota

_____ 4. most common fungi phylum; includes yeast

D. Deuteromycota

_____ 5. includes mushrooms

E. Zygomycota

In your textbook, read about reproduction in common molds.

Label the diagram of a common mold. Use these choices:

mating strains	**rhizoids**	**sporangia**	**spores**	**stolons**

6. _____

7. _____

8. _____

9. _____

10. _____

Use each of the terms above only once to complete the passage.

Hyphae called **(11)** _____ penetrate the food, anchor the mycelium, and absorb

nutrients. Asexual **(12)** _____ germinate on a food source, and hyphae begin to

grow. Hyphae called **(13)** _____ grow across the surface of the food source and

form a mycelium. Special hyphae grow upward to form **(14)** _____ that are filled

with asexual spores. In sexual reproduction, parts of two haploid **(15)** _____

fuse to form a diploid structure.

Copyright © Glencoe/McGraw-Hill, a division of The McGraw-Hill Companies, Inc.

In your textbook, read about sac fungi, club fungi, and other fungi.

In the space at the left, write the letter of the term or phrase that best completes each statement.

_____ 16. Most members of the phylum Ascomycota are _____
         A. aquatic.   C. multicellular.
         B. molds.   D. unicellular.

_____ 17. Sac fungi produce spore-bearing hyphae called _____
         A. ascospores.   C. gametangia.
         B. conidiophores.   D. zygomycetes.

_____ 18. The ascus of a sac fungi _____
         A. develops into a haploid mycellium.   C. is where the hyphae develop.
         B. is a saclike structure where spores develop.   D. produces four haploid nuclei.

_____ 19. The fruiting body of a club fungi is called a _____
         A. basidiocarp.   C. sac.
         B. gametangium.   D. stolon.

_____ 20. The rapid growth of basidiocarps is due to _____
         A. cell division.   C. meiotic division.
         B. cell enlargement.   D. water intake.

_____ 21. Saprophytic basidiocarps produce enzymes that _____
         A. are beneficial for plants.   C. make bread dough rise.
         B. decompose wood.   D. suggest they are related to protists.

_____ 22. Another name for the deuteromycetes is _____
         A. club fungi.   C. imperfect fungi.
         B. common molds.   D. sac fungi.

In your textbook, read about club fungi and the life cycle of a mushroom.

Label the diagram of the mushroom and parts of its life cycle. Use these choices:

        basidium   **caps**   **spores**

23. _____

24. _____

25. _____

Copyright © Glencoe/McGraw-Hill, a division of The McGraw-Hill Companies, Inc.

Study Guide

CHAPTER 20

Section 3: Ecology of Fungi

In your textbook, read about fungi and photosynthesizers.

Complete the Venn diagram by writing the number of each phrase in the appropriate place. These phrases may be used more than once.

1. associated with plant roots
2. important for soil formation
3. important for agricultural crops
4. associated with a green alga or cyanobacterium
5. obtain nutrients from photosynthesizing partner
6. mutualistic relationship between fungi and other organism
7. fungus that absorbs and concentrates minerals and increases root surface area for plant
8. fungus that provides a dense web of hyphae in which algae or cyanobacterium can grow

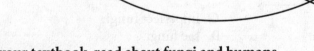

Mycorrhizae   **Lichens**

Both

In your textbook, read about fungi and humans.

If the statement is true, write true. *If the statement is false, replace the italicized word or phrase to make it true.*

9. Penicillin is a drug that comes from a fungus. Another fungus is the source of *anti-headache drugs* for organ transplant patients.

_____

10. People eat fungi such as truffles, mushrooms, and the yeast in bread. Fungi also give flavor to *cheeses and cola drinks.*

_____

11. *Respiration* produces airy bread and the alcohol in beer and wine.

_____

12. The use of fungi and bacteria to remove pollution is called *enviroremediation.*

_____

Copyright © Glencoe/McGraw-Hill, a division of The McGraw-Hill Companies, Inc.

Guía de estudio

En tu libro de texto, lee acerca de las características de los hongos.

Relaciona la definición de la columna A con el término de la columna B.

Columna A		Columna B
_____	**1.** cuerpo de un hongo en forma de malla	**A.** cuerpo fructífero
_____	**2.** paredes entre las celdas fúngicas	**B.** hifas
_____	**3.** filamentos en un hongo multicelular	**C.** micelio
_____	**4.** hongo unicelular	**D.** septa
_____	**5.** estructura fúngica reproductiva	**E.** levadura

En tu libro de texto, lee acerca de la nutrición de los hongos.

Completa la tabla marcando la(s) columna(s) correcta(s) para cada característica.

Características de los hongos	Hongos saprofitos	Hongos parasíticos	Hongos mutualistas
6. Nocivos para el huésped			
7. Útiles para el huésped ·			
8. Heterótrofos			
9. Reductores de basura orgánica			
10. Simbiosis			

En tu libro de texto, lee acerca de la reproducción de los hongos.

Escribe el término que mejor complete cada afirmación. Usa estas opciones:

asexualmente   esporangios   meiosis   supervivencia   viento

11. Los hongos se reproducen _____ mediante la fragmentación, al germinar o producir esporas.

12. Producir un gran número de esporas aumenta las probabilidades de _____ de las especies.

13. Las esporas fúngicas pueden dispersarse a través de los animales, el agua y el _____ .

14. Los _____ protegen las esporas y evitan que se sequen hasta que se liberen.

15. Los hongos podrían producir esporas mediante la _____ o la mitosis.

Copyright © Glencoe/McGraw-Hill, a division of The McGraw-Hill Companies, Inc.

Guía de estudio

En tu libro de texto, lee acerca de la diversidad de los hongos.

Relaciona la definición de la columna A con el término de la columna B.

Columna A

_____ 1. incluyen el moho del pan y otros mohos

_____ 2. parecen carecer de una etapa sexual en el ciclo de vida

_____ 3. producen esporas flageladas

_____ 4. el filo de hongo más común; incluyen la levadura

_____ 5. incluyen los hongos comestibles

Columna B

A. Ascomicetes

B. Basidiomicetes

C. Quitridiomicetes

D. Deuteromicetes

E. Zigomicetes

En tu libro de texto, lee acerca de la reproducción en los mohos comunes.

Identifica las partes del diagrama de un moho común. Usa estas opciones:

cepas fecundantes   esporangios   esporas   estolones   rizoides

6. _____

7. _____

8. _____

9. _____

10. _____

Usa cada uno de los términos anteriores una vez únicamente para completar el párrafo.

Las hifas llamadas **(11)** _____ penetran en el alimento, se anclan en el micelio y absorben nutrientes. Las **(12)** _____ asexuales germinan en una fuente de alimento y las hifas empiezan a crecer. Las hifas llamadas **(13)** _____ crecen en la superficie del alimento y forman un micelio. Las hifas especiales crecen hacia arriba hasta formar **(14)** _____ , los cuales están llenos de esporas asexuales. En la reproducción sexual, las partes de las dos **(15)** _____ haploides se fusionan para formar una estructura diploide.

Copyright © Glencoe/McGraw-Hill, a division of The McGraw-Hill Companies, Inc.

En tu libro de texto, lee acerca de los hongos saculares, hongos de palo y otros hongos.

En el espacio a la izquierda, escribe la letra del término o frase que mejor complete cada afirmación.

_____ **16.** La mayoría de los miembros del filo ascomicetes son _____
        A. acuáticos.   **C.** multicelulares.
        B. mohos.   **D.** unicelulares.

_____ **17.** Los hongos saculares producen hifas portadoras de esporas llamadas _____
        A. ascosporas.   **C.** gametangios.
        B. conidióforos.   **D.** zigomicetes.

_____ **18.** El ascomiceto de un hongo sacular _____
        A. es donde las hifas se desarrollan.
        B. es una estructura en forma de saco donde las esporas se desarrollan.
        C. produce cuatro núcleos haploides.
        D. se convierte en un micelio haploide.

_____ **19.** El cuerpo fructífero de un hongo de palo se llama _____
        A. basidiocarpo.   **C.** estolón.
        B. bolsa.   **D.** gametangio.

_____ **20.** El crecimiento rápido de los basidiocarpos se debe a _____
        A. el agrandamiento celular.   **C.** la división meiótica.
        B. la división celular.   **D.** la ingesta de agua.

_____ **21.** Los basidiocarpos saprofíticos producen enzimas que _____
        A. descomponen la madera.
        B. hacen que la masa de pan crezca.
        C. indican que están relacionadas con los protistas.
        D. son de beneficio para las plantas.

_____ **22.** Otro nombre para los deuteromicetes es _____
        A. hongos de palo.   **C.** hongos saculares.
        B. hongos imperfectos.   **D.** mohos comunes.

En tu libro de texto, lee acerca de los hongos de palo y el ciclo de vida de un hongo seta.

Identifica el diagrama del hongo seta y las partes de su ciclo de vida. Usa estas opciones:

    basidio   **capuchones**   **esporas**

23. _____

24. _____

25. _____

Copyright © Glencoe/McGraw-Hill, a division of The McGraw-Hill Companies, Inc.

Guía de estudio

CAPÍTULO 20

Sección 3: Ecología de los hongos

En tu libro de texto, lee acerca de los hongos y los fotosintetizadores.

Completa el diagrama de Venn con los números de las siguientes frases en la ubicación correcta. Las frases se pueden usar más de una vez.

1. importantes para los cultivos agrícolas

2. importantes para la formación del suelo

3. tienen relación con las raíces de las plantas

4. tienen relación con algas verdes o cianobacterias

5. relación mutualista entre hongos y otro organismo

6. obtienen nutrientes de un compañero fotosintetizador

7. hongo que absorbe y concentra minerales y aumenta el área superficial de la raíz para la planta

8. hongo que ofrece una red densa de hifas en la cual las algas o las cianobacterias pueden crecer

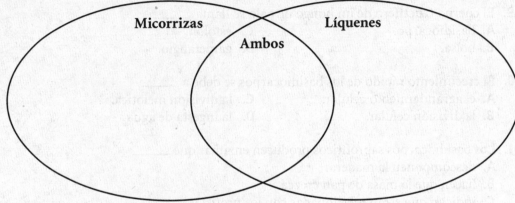

En tu libro de texto, lee acerca de los hongos y los seres humanos.

Si la afirmación es verdadera, escribe «verdadero». Si la afirmación es falsa, sustituye la palabra o frase para volverla verdadera.

9. La penicilina es un fármaco que proviene de un hongo. Otro hongo es la fuente de *fármacos contra los dolores de cabeza* para pacientes de transplante de órganos.

_____

10. Las personas comen hongos como las trufas, las setas y la levadura en el pan. Los hongos también dan sabor a *los quesos y a las bebidas cola*.

_____

11. La *respiración* produce pan esponjado y el alcohol en la cerveza y el vino.

_____

12. El uso de hongos y bacterias para eliminar la contaminación se denomina *remediación ambiental*.

_____

Copyright © Glencoe/McGraw-Hill, a division of The McGraw-Hill Companies, Inc.

Section
Quick Check

CHAPTER 20
Section 1: Characteristics of Fungi

After reading the section in your textbook, respond to each statement.

1. Tell how yeasts are different from other fungi.

_____

2. Explain how extensive hyphae are an advantage to fungi.

_____

_____

_____

3. Describe multicellular fungi in a sentence. Use the terms *hyphae*, *mycelium*, and *fruiting body* in your answer.

_____

_____

_____

4. Distinguish the functions of spores and sporophores in fungi.

_____

_____

_____

5. Evaluate the role of saprophytic fungi in the environment.

_____

_____

_____

_____

Copyright © Glencoe/McGraw-Hill, a division of The McGraw-Hill Companies, Inc.

Section
Quick Check

Section 2: Diversity of Fungi

After reading the section in your textbook, respond to each statement.

1. State the two criteria scientists use to divide fungi into phyla.

_____

_____

2. Identify the phylum that contains only unicellular fungi.

_____

3. Contrast an ascocarp and a basidiocarp.

_____

_____

_____

4. Summarize the process of sexual reproduction in fungi.

_____

_____

_____

_____

5. Predict how the numbers of species of deuteromycetes and ascomycetes are likely
to change over time.

_____

_____

_____

Copyright © Glencoe/McGraw-Hill, a division of The McGraw-Hill Companies, Inc.

Section
Quick Check

Section 3: Ecology of Fungi

After reading the section in your textbook, respond to each statement.

1. Name two kinds of mutualistic relationships that involve fungi.

_____

_____

2. Explain how mycorrhizae are beneficial to plants.

_____

_____

_____

3. Describe how fungi are used in bioremediation.

_____

_____

_____

4. Differentiate the roles of the fungus and the alga (also called cyanobacterium) in lichens.

_____

_____

5. Speculate about the importance of harmful fungi in ecosystems.

_____

_____

_____

Copyright © Glencoe/McGraw-Hill, a division of The McGraw-Hill Companies, Inc.

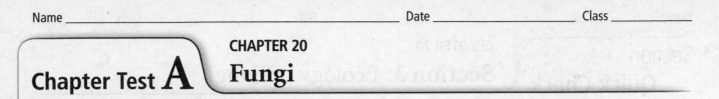

Chapter Test A

CHAPTER 20
Fungi

Part A: Multiple Choice

In the space at the left, write the letter of the phrase or sentence that best answers each question.

_____ **1.** Which is a characteristic of fungi?
A. form unicellular colonies
B. have cells with a nucleus
C. have short life spans
D. make food using photosynthesis

_____ **2.** Which is an example of fungi reproduction?
A. A broken mycelium grows a new mushroom.
B. During budding, a yeast cell forms spores.
C. Lichen fungi produce egg and sperm cells.
D. Mold produces seeds for new mold to grow.

_____ **3.** Which fungi would be the first to grow back after a volcanic eruption destroyed all the life on a tundra plain?
A. parasitic yeast
B. photosynthesizing mold
C. pioneer lichen
D. saprophytic mushrooms

Part B: Matching

Write the letter of the correct term on the line next to the description. Answers may be used only once.

_____ **1.** common kitchen fungi with two types of hyphae

_____ **2.** aquatic fungi with flagella on their spores

_____ **3.** yeast used to make bread

A. chytrid

B. mold

C. sac fungi

Part C: Interpreting Drawings

*Use **Figure 1** to respond to the following statement.*

1. Identify parts *A*, *B*, and *C* of this structure.

A. _____

B. _____

C. _____

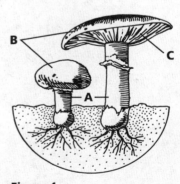

Figure 1

Copyright © Glencoe/McGraw-Hill, a division of The McGraw-Hill Companies, Inc.

Chapter Test A CONTINUED

Use **Figure 2** to respond to each statement.

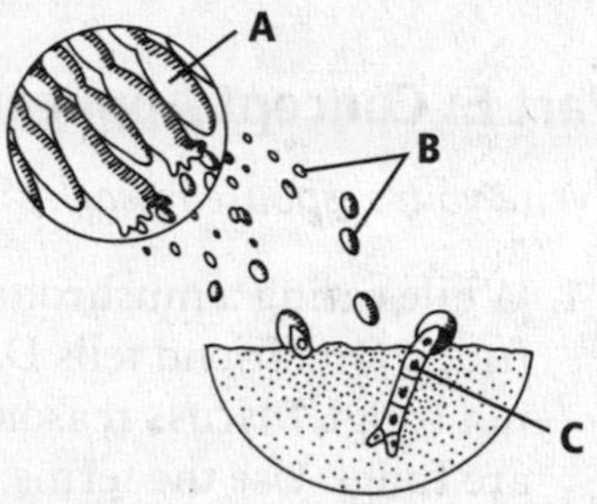

2. **Identify** the parts labeled *A*, *B*, and *C*.

A. _____

B. _____

C. _____

3. **Explain** what is happening in the drawing.

Figure 2

_____

_____

_____

_____

_____

Part D: Short Answer

Write your response to each question and statement in the space provided.

1. **Contrast** saprophytic, parasitic, and mutualistic fungi.

_____

_____

_____

2. **Describe** What is a lichen? Include the term *symbiotic* in your answer.

_____

_____

_____

_____

Copyright © Glencoe/McGraw-Hill, a division of The McGraw-Hill Companies, Inc.

Chapter Test A CONTINUED

Part E: Concept Application

Write your response to each statement in the space provided.

1. While eating a mushroom pizza, David asks his friends if they are enjoying the fungi. One friend tells David that mushrooms are plants like tomatoes or corn and not fungi. **Discuss** reasons David could use to convince his friend that mushrooms are fungi. Use the terms *chitin, cellulose, hyphae,* and *septa* in your discussion.

_____

_____

_____

2. A new tourist town is being planned and built in a remote forest. The town will be the center of tourist activities such as camping, hiking, skiing, rafting, and mountain biking. Part of the infrastructure being planned for the town is roads to accommodate tourist traffic and delivery trucks. A coal burning plant will also be built to provide the town with electricity. **Infer** why local biologists will be monitoring the lichens that grow on forest trees in the coming years. Use the term *bioindicator* in your answer.

_____

_____

_____

Copyright © Glencoe/McGraw-Hill, a division of The McGraw-Hill Companies, Inc.

Chapter Test **B**

CHAPTER 20
Fungi

Part A: Multiple Choice

In the space at the left, write the letter of the term or phrase that best answers each question.

_____ 1. Which describes fungi?
- **A.** eukaryotic autotroph
- **B.** eukaryotic heterotroph
- **C.** prokaryotic autotroph
- **D.** prokaryotic heterotroph

_____ 2. Which are unicellular fungi?
- **A.** lichens
- **B.** mold
- **C.** puffballs
- **D.** yeast

_____ 3. Which is an example of mutualistic fungi?
- **A.** athlete's foot fungus absorbing nutrients from cells
- **B.** bread mold reproducing to cover a slice of bread
- **C.** fungi and plant roots cooperating to meet their needs
- **D.** mushroom fruiting bodies sprouting from tree roots

_____ 4. Which statement describes lichens?
- **A.** autotrophic organisms and fungi in a mutualistic relationship
- **B.** photosynthesizing fungi that can live in harsh environmental conditions
- **C.** saprophytic fungi that secretes acids to grow on and colonize rocks
- **D.** two heterotrophic fungi species that thrive on nutrients from the air

Part B: Matching and Completion

Matching *Write the letter of the correct term on the line next to its description. Answers may be used once or not at all.*

_____ 1. A broken hypha tossed into a compost pile grows into a new fungus.

_____ 2. A yeast cell pinches off part of its body to form a daughter cell.

_____ 3. A fungus produces a reproductive cell with a tough outer covering.

- **A.** budding
- **B.** fragmentation
- **C.** spore production
- **D.** sexual reproduction

Completion *Write the term or phrase that best completes each statement.*

4. The phylum containing aquatic fungi with spores that grow flagella is

_____ .

5. The phylum containing a fungus that is a favorite pizza topping is _____ .

Copyright © Glencoe/McGraw-Hill, a division of The McGraw-Hill Companies, Inc.

Chapter Test B CONTINUED

6. Yeasts are classified in phylum _____ .

7. Refrigeration is a process used to slow the growth of fungi in phylum
_____ .

Part C: Interpreting Drawings

Use **Figure 1** *to respond to each statement.*

1. Identify parts *A*, *B*, and *C* of this structure. **Infer** the purpose of
structure *C*.

A. _____

B. _____

C. _____

_____

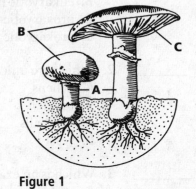

Figure 1

2. Infer the environmental conditions that encourage the appearance of the
structure. **Describe** these conditions.

_____

_____

_____

Use **Figure 2** *to respond to the following statement.*

3. Study the drawing. **Identify** the parts labeled *A*, *B*, and *C*.

A. _____

B. _____

C. _____

Figure 2

Part D: Short Answer

Write your response to each statement in the space provided.

1. Describe the basic physical structures of fungi. Include the terms *hyphae*,
mycelium, and *fruiting body* in your answer.

_____

_____

Copyright © Glencoe/McGraw-Hill, a division of The McGraw-Hill Companies, Inc.

Chapter Test B CONTINUED

2. Infer the role saprophytic fungi play in a forest ecosystem.

_____

_____

_____

3. Discuss how the production and design of puffball spores lessens the threat of predation and helps the spores resist harsh environmental conditions.

_____

_____

_____

Part E: Concept Application

Write your response to each statement in the space provided.

1. A research scientist has developed a chemical that prevents the growth of mold rhizoids, but the chemical does not inhibit the growth of stolons. **Infer** the chemical's effect on the growth of bread molds if the substance were applied to a loaf of bread.

_____

_____

_____

2. Hypothesize how fungi could be helpful in the development of future technologies that treat severely polluted water. Include the term *bioremediation* in your discussion.

_____

_____

_____

3. Infer a potential negative effect of fungi on the timber industry.

_____

_____

_____

Copyright © Glencoe/McGraw-Hill, a division of The McGraw-Hill Companies, Inc.

Chapter Test **C**

CHAPTER 20
Fungi

Part A: Multiple Choice

In the space at the left, write the letter of the term, phrase, or sentence that best answers each question.

_____ 1. Which describes organisms in kingdom Fungi?
A. autotrophic eukaryotes
B. autotrophic saprophytes
C. heterotrophic eukaryotes
D. heterotrophic saprophytes

_____ 2. Which is an advantage of fragmentation?
A. Broken fungi can reproduce new mycelium.
B. Daughter cells will easily pinch off parent cells.
C. Fungi can produce a greater number of spores.
D. Torn hyphae can easily repair injured tissues.

_____ 3. Members of which phylum of fungi were once classified as protists?
A. Ascomycota
B. Chytridiomycota
C. Deuteromycota
D. Zygomycota

_____ 4. Which phylum classifies a type of fungi essential to the vineyards and winery businesses of California?
A. Ascomycota
B. Basidiomycota
C. Chytridiomycota
D. Zygomycota

_____ 5. What do the fungi of lichens provide to their photosynthetic partners?
A. acid for creating cyanobacteria habitats
B. food from photosynthesis
C. protective outer covering
D. structural support for the cyanobacteria

_____ 6. Which would be an application of bioremediation?
A. considering symbiotic fungi when planting new forests
B. developing drugs from a new fungus species
C. using fungi to remove pollutants from water
D. using saprophytic fungi to decompose organic wastes

Part B: Completion

Write the term or phrase that best completes each statement.

1. Unicellular fungi found in substances containing sugar are called _____ .

2. The primary body components of fungi are called _____ .

Copyright © Glencoe/McGraw-Hill, a division of The McGraw-Hill Companies, Inc.

Chapter Test C CONTINUED

3. Fungi growing on the roots of trees that receive food from the tree but also help the plant absorb nutrients are called _____ .

4. Structures that divide hyphae into individual cells are called _____ .

5. The mold structures that enables a fungus to spread across the surface of leftover spaghetti sauce are called _____ .

6. Many forest ecosystems depend on a mutualistic relationship called _____ .

Part C: Interpreting Drawings

*Use **Figure 1** to respond to the following statement.*

1. Identify the fungus structure drawn and the structure's primary function. **Describe** how the parts of this structure enable it to fulfill its function.

_____

_____

_____

_____

_____

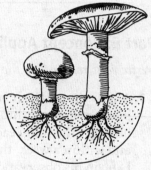

Figure 1

*Use **Figure 2** to respond to the following statement.*

2. Identify the fungus parts in the drawing.

_____

_____

_____

Figure 2

Part D: Short Answer

Write your response to each statement in the space provided.

1. Describe the composition of cell walls in fungi.

_____

_____

_____

_____

Copyright © Glencoe/McGraw-Hill, a division of The McGraw-Hill Companies, Inc.

Chapter Test C continued

2. **Compare** and **contrast** how different types of fungi obtain nutrients.

_____

_____

_____

3. **Hypothesize** about the effects of damaged sporangia in black bread mold.

_____

_____

_____

Part E: Concept Application

Write your response to the following statement in the space provided.

1. A heavy rain falls in a forest, and within hours, a mycologist observes large, bright yellow mushrooms sprouting from the base of an old tree. The scientist observes the fungi each day for a week. The mushrooms shrivel within a few days, and within a week, there is no trace of them. **Analyze** the mycologist's observations. **Explain** his observations considering the body structures and life cycles of fungi.

_____

_____

_____

Use the description below to respond to each statement.

Two hundred years ago, miners would take caged canaries into coal mineshafts as they worked. Being smaller, the canaries would succumb to odorless, toxic gases before the gases would affect humans. As the miners worked, they watched the canaries. If the canaries suddenly died, it was a warning for the miners to leave the mineshaft.

2. **Compare** Form an analogy between the canaries used in coal mines and the lichens living in tundra ecosystems.

_____

_____

_____

3. **Formulate** a strategy for using lichens as Earth's "canaries in a coal mine."

_____

_____

_____

Copyright © Glencoe/McGraw-Hill, a division of The McGraw-Hill Companies, Inc.

CHAPTER 20
Assessment   **Student Recording Sheet**

Section 20.1

Vocabulary Review

Write the vocabulary term that makes each sentence true.

1. _____   2. _____   3. _____

Understand Key Concepts

Select the best answer from the choices given, and fill in the corresponding circle.

4. Ⓐ Ⓑ Ⓒ Ⓓ   6. Ⓐ Ⓑ Ⓒ Ⓓ   8. Ⓐ Ⓑ Ⓒ Ⓓ

5. Ⓐ Ⓑ Ⓒ Ⓓ   7. Ⓐ Ⓑ Ⓒ Ⓓ

Constructed Response

9. _____

_____

10. _____

_____

11. Record your answer for question 11 on a separate sheet of paper.

Think Critically

12. _____

_____

_____

13. _____

_____

_____

Section 20.2

Vocabulary Review

Explain the difference between the vocabulary terms in each pair.

14. _____

_____

_____

15. _____

_____

_____

Copyright © Glencoe/McGraw-Hill, a division of The McGraw-Hill Companies, Inc.

CHAPTER 20
Assessment | Student Recording Sheet

16. _____

_____

_____

Understand Key Concepts

Select the best answer from the choices given, and fill in the corresponding circle.

17. Ⓐ Ⓑ Ⓒ Ⓓ   **19.** Ⓐ Ⓑ Ⓒ Ⓓ   **21.** Ⓐ Ⓑ Ⓒ Ⓓ

18. Ⓐ Ⓑ Ⓒ Ⓓ   **20.** Ⓐ Ⓑ Ⓒ Ⓓ

Constructed Response

22. _____

_____

_____

_____

_____

23. Record your answer for question 23 on a separate piece of paper.

24. Record your answer for question 24 on a separate piece of paper.

Think Critically

25.–26. Record your answers for questions 25 and 26 on a separate sheet of paper.

Section 20.3

Vocabulary Review

Write the vocabulary term that best answers each question.

27. _____ **28.** _____ **29.** _____

Understand Key Concepts

Select the best answer from the choices given, and fill in the corresponding circle.

30. Ⓐ Ⓑ Ⓒ Ⓓ   **31.** Ⓐ Ⓑ Ⓒ Ⓓ   **32.** Ⓐ Ⓑ Ⓒ Ⓓ

Constructed Response

33. _____

_____

34. _____

_____

Copyright © Glencoe/McGraw-Hill, a division of The McGraw-Hill Companies, Inc.

CHAPTER 20
Assessment   Student Recording Sheet

Think Critically

35. _____

_____

36. Record your answer for question 36 on a separate sheet of paper.

37. Careers in Biology Record your answer for question 37 on a separate sheet of paper.

38. Record your answer for question 38 on a separate sheet of paper.

39. _____

_____

_____

Additional Assessment

40. Writing in Biology Record your answer for question 40 on a separate sheet of paper.

Document-Based Questions

41. _____

_____

_____

_____

42. _____

_____

_____

_____

43. _____

_____

Cumulative Review

44. _____

_____

_____

_____

Copyright © Glencoe/McGraw-Hill, a division of The McGraw-Hill Companies, Inc.

CHAPTER 20
Assessment | **Student Recording Sheet**

Standardized Test Practice

Multiple Choice

Select the best answer from the choices given, and fill in the corresponding circle.

1. Ⓐ Ⓑ Ⓒ Ⓓ   3. Ⓐ Ⓑ Ⓒ Ⓓ   5. Ⓐ Ⓑ Ⓒ Ⓓ   7. Ⓐ Ⓑ Ⓒ Ⓓ

2. Ⓐ Ⓑ Ⓒ Ⓓ   4. Ⓐ Ⓑ Ⓒ Ⓓ   6. Ⓐ Ⓑ Ⓒ Ⓓ   8. Ⓐ Ⓑ Ⓒ Ⓓ

Short Answer

Answer each question with complete sentences.

9. _____

   _____

   _____

10. Record your answer for question 10 on a separate sheet of paper.

11. _____

   _____

12. _____

   _____

13. _____

   _____

14. _____

   _____

Extended Response

Answer each question with complete sentences.

15. Record your answer for question 15 on a separate sheet of paper.

16. _____

   _____

17. _____

   _____

18. _____

   _____

Essay Question

19. Record your answer for question 19 on a separate sheet of paper.

Copyright © Glencoe/McGraw-Hill, a division of The McGraw-Hill Companies, Inc.

Diagnostic Test

Page 4

1. The correct answer is D. Based on student responses, use the list below to address preconceptions.

   • **Student thinks bacteria have nuclei and are eukaryotes.** Direct student to the diversity of prokaryotes discussion in Section 18.1.

   • **Student thinks bacteria have the same complex organelles as eukaryotic cells.** Direct student to the structure of prokaryotes discussion in Section 18.1.

   • **Student thinks bacteria lack DNA.** Direct student to the structure of prokaryotes discussion in Section 18.1.

   • **Student thinks only protist cells have flagella.** Direct student to the identifying prokaryotes discussion in Section 18.1.

2. The correct answer is B. Based on student responses, use the list below to address preconceptions.

   • **Student thinks bacteria are not responsible for recycling nutrients.** Direct student to the ecology of bacteria discussion in Section 18.1.

   • **Student thinks soil bacteria have symbiotic relationship with trees.** Explain that fungi have symbiotic relationships with trees and absorb water and nutrients for tree roots, but bacteria do not have these types of relationships.

   • **Student thinks soil bacteria are found in the digestive tract of soil organisms.** Explain that many organisms such as humans and termites have symbiotic relationships with bacteria living in their digestive tracts, but soil bacteria live in soil and not in organisms' digestive tracts.

   • **Student thinks soil bacteria are large enough to be a food source for invertebrates.** Direct student to the structure of prokaryotes discussion in Section 18.1.

3. Diseases caused by viral infections include AIDS (HIV), genital herpes, measles, mumps, chicken pox, common cold, influenza, warts, shingles, polio, viral meningitis, rabies, smallpox, and hepatitis. Based on student responses, use the list below to address preconceptions.

   • **Student confuses bacterial infections with viral infections.** Direct student to the human bacterial disease chart in Section 18.1 and the viral disease chart in Section 18.2.

   • **Student confuses body diseases such as asthma and cancer with viral infections.** Direct student to the viral disease chart in Section 18.2.

   • **Student thinks viruses are living organisms.** Direct student to the viruses discussion in Section 18.2.

   • **Student confuses viruses and bacteria.** Direct student to the diversity of prokaryotes discussion in Section 18.1 and the viruses discussion in Section 18.2.

Launch Lab

Page 5 • What are the differences between animal cells and bacterial cells?

Analysis

1. Students should observe that the animal cell has characteristics of a eukaryotic cell, whereas the bacterial cell contains characteristics found in a prokaryotic cell.

2. Yes, animal and bacterial cells are living things because they can live independently.

MiniLab

Page 6 • Classify Bacteria

Analysis

1. Answers will vary. Sample hypothesis: Bacteria might be differentiated by differences in their structure or shape.

2. Answers will vary. Students might describe cocci as round, bacilli as oblong, and spirochetes as spiral shaped.

BioLab: Design Your Own

Page 7 • How can the most effective antibiotics be determined?

Analyze and Conclude

1. Results will depend on the antibiotic disks and bacterial cultures used. Most of the antibiotic disks should show inhibition zones. Untreated control disks should have no inhibition zones.

Copyright © Glencoe/McGraw-Hill, a division of The McGraw-Hill Companies, Inc.

2. Not completing the treatment can allow the bacteria that have survived to rebound and make a person ill again, and surviving bacteria can develop resistance to the antibiotic.

3. Answers will vary; antibiotic might work in an agar culture but not in humans.

4. Answers will vary. Sources of error include using expired antibiotic disks, contaminating antibiotic disks, contaminating bacterial cultures due to unsterile procedures, and misidentifying antibiotic disks.

Real-World Biology: Analysis

Page 9 • Prion Diseases

Planning the Activity

Have students complete this activity after they have studied prions in Chapter 18 of the text.

Purpose

Students will investigate the spread of chronic wasting disease in deer and elk and concerns about the disease.

Career Applications

An interest in chronic wasting disease or other diseases of wildlife can lead to a career working on a team of wildlife disease experts. Among the scientists on these teams are wildlife biologists, wildlife veterinarians, veterinary technicians, and wildlife technicians. These teams can provide rapid assistance to areas with an outbreak of disease, test for disease, determine the cause of disease, determine the impact on animal populations and humans, and do research on disease. Some work is done in laboratories, but other work takes place where the animals live. These teams usually work for the federal or state government.

Teaching Strategies

• Ask students "What do you know about prion diseases?" and "What do you know about mad cow disease?"

• Have students discuss where they have seen deer and elk.

• If deer or elk in your state have chronic wasting disease, find out what guidelines or laws your state has to help control the spread of the disease.

• Below Level: Use a map of the United States and/or draw a flowchart on the board to help students understand how CWD spread from its point of origin.

• Above Level: Have students who want a challenge draw a map of the United States showing the spread of CWD over time.

Answers to Student Worksheet

Part A: The Spread of Chronic Wasting Disease
Analyze and Conclude

1. Answers will vary. Answers could include that CWD spread from captive deer and elk in a small area, to wild deer and elk in a small area, and then to captive and wild deer and elk in a large area.

2. Answers will vary. Answers could include suggestions such as making sure any animals that are brought into the state are free from CWD and improving the fencing in facilities and farms that have deer or elk to keep them from escaping.

Part B: Concerns About Chronic Wasting Disease
Analyze and Conclude

1. Answers will vary. Answers could include that feeding deer leads to a higher concentration of deer in one area. This increases the chances of a diseased deer transmitting the disease to healthy deer.

2. Answers will vary. Recommendations could include not eating the meat from the hunted deer and elk or having the hunted animals tested and only eating the meat if the animals are free from CWD.

Careers in Biology

Wildlife disease experts can provide rapid assistance to areas with an outbreak of disease, test for disease, determine the cause of disease, determine the impact on animal populations and humans, and do research on disease.

Copyright © Glencoe/McGraw-Hill, a division of The McGraw-Hill Companies, Inc.

Enrichment

Page 11 • Human Bacterial and Viral Diseases

Student articles will vary but should be clearly written and accurate. All questions posed in the class discussions should be thoroughly researched, and answers should be supported by the research. All sources must be accurately cited.

Concept Mapping

Page 12 • Viral Infections

1. host cell
2. genetic material
3. cytoplasm
4. lysogenic cycle
5. host cell chromosome
6. dormant
7. lytic cycle
8. viral genes
9. protein coat
10. exocytosis

Study Guide

Page 13 • Section 18.1

1. Student answers may vary. *Same:* Eubacteria and archaebacteria are both prokaryotes. *Different:* Eubacteria have strong cell walls containing peptidoglycan, and archaebacteria do not. They each have different lipids in their plasma membranes, as well as different ribosomal proteins and RNA. Archaebacteria predominate in extreme environments.

2. Student answers may vary. *Same:* Thermoacidophiles and halophiles are both archaebacteria that occupy extreme environments. *Different:* Thermoacidophiles thrive in hot, acidic environments. Halophiles occupy salty environments. Most thermoacidophiles are anaerobes; most halophiles are aerobic.

3. flagella
4. pili
5. plasma membrane
6. chromosome
7. capsule

8. cell wall
9. C
10. D
11. A
12. B
13. Student drawings should show spherical prokaryotes.
14. Student drawings should show rod-shaped prokaryotes.
15. Student drawings should show spiral-shaped prokaryotes.
16. bacteria
17. decomposers
18. nitrogen
19. nitrogen fixation
20. normal flora
21. symbiotically
22. vitamin K
23. yogurt
24. antibiotics
25. disease

Page 15 • Section 18.2

1. C
2. H
3. A
4. D
5. F
6. B
7. G
8. E
9. Lytic Cycle
10. Lytic Cycle, Lysogenic Cycle
11. Lytic Cycle, Lysogenic Cycle
12. Lysogenic Cycle
13. Lytic Cycle, Lysogenic Cycle
14. Lysogenic Cycle
15. RNA
16. retrovirus
17. human immunodeficiency virus (HIV)
18. cancer-causing
19. reverse transcriptase

Copyright © Glencoe/McGraw-Hill, a division of The McGraw-Hill Companies, Inc.

20. DNA
21. nucleus
22. host cell
23. Prions
24. Viruses
25. Viruses
26. Prions
27. Viruses, Prions
28. Prions
29. Viruses
30. piece of paper folded many times
31. true
32. brain

Guía de estudio

Página 17 • Sección 18.1

1. Las respuestas de los estudiantes pueden variar. *Semejanza:* Tanto las eubacterias como las arqueobacterias son procariotas. *Diferencia:* Las eubacterias tienen paredes celulares fuertes que contienen peptidoglicano mientras que las arqueobacterias no. Cada una tiene diferentes lípidos en sus membranas plasmáticas, así como diferentes proteínas ribosomales y ARN. Las arqueobacterias predominan en ambientes extremos.

2. Las respuestas de los estudiantes pueden variar. *Semejanza:* Tanto los termoacidófilos como los halófilos son arqueobacterias que ocupan ambientes extremos. *Diferencia:* Los termoacidófilos proliferan en ambientes calientes, ácidos. Los halófilos ocupan ambientes salados. La mayoría de los termoacidófilos son anaerobios; la mayoría de los halófilos son aerobios.

3. flagelos
4. pelos
5. membrana plasmática
6. cromosoma
7. cápsula
8. pared celular
9. C
10. D
11. A

12. B
13. Los dibujos de los estudiantes deben mostrar procariotas esféricas.
14. Los dibujos de los estudiantes deben mostrar procariotas en forma de varilla.
15. Los dibujos de los estudiantes deben mostrar procariotas en forma de espiral.
16. bacterias
17. descomponedores
18. nitrógeno
19. fijación de nitrógeno
20. flora normal
21. simbióticamente
22. vitamina K
23. yogurt
24. antibióticos
25. enfermedades

Página 19 • Sección 18.2

1. C
2. H
3. A
4. D
5. F
6. B
7. G
8. E
9. Ciclo lítico
10. Ciclo lítico, ciclo lisogénico
11. Ciclo lítico, ciclo lisogénico
12. Ciclo lisogénico
13. Ciclo lítico, ciclo lisogénico
14. Ciclo lisogénico
15. ARN
16. retrovirus
17. virus de inmunodeficiencia humana (VIH)
18. causan cáncer
19. transcriptasa inversa
20. ADN
21. núcleo
22. célula huésped
23. Priones

Copyright © Glencoe/McGraw-Hill, a division of The McGraw-Hill Companies, Inc.

24. Virus
25. Virus
26. Priones
27. Virus, Priones
28. Priones
29. Virus
31. pedazo de papel doblado varias veces
32. verdadero
33. cerebro

Section Quick Check

Page 21 • Section 18.1

1. Some prokaryotes take in preformed nutrients. Others use sunlight to synthesize organic molecules. A third type breaks down and releases inorganic compounds.

2. Pili help a bacterial cell attach to an environmental surface or transfer plasmids between bacterial cells.

3. Prokaryotes are small unicellular organisms with no organelles. Their genes are in an area of the cell called the nucleoid. They have a polysaccharide capsule around their cell wall.

4. They both are simple cells with no organelles. The cell walls of the eubacteria contain peptidoglycan, but the cell walls of the archaebacteria do not. They also have different lipids, different ribosomal proteins, and different RNA.

5. Each bacterial cell usually produces only one spore, so the total number of bacterial cells remains the same. Reproduction would increase the number of bacterial cells.

Page 22 • Section 18.2

1. A prion (proteinaceous infectious protein) is a protein that can cause infection or disease.

2. The outer layer of a virus is a capsid made of proteins. The capsid surrounds either RNA or DNA.

3. Answers will vary. Viruses cannot replicate by themselves. They require a host cell. Therefore, cells must already exist for viruses to reproduce.

4. The virus attaches to the host cell, and the genetic material enters the cytoplasm. The virus replicates by either the lytic cycle or the lysogenic cycle.

5. In the lytic cycle, the viral DNA or RNA might be replicated immediately and does not result in permanent changes in the DNA of the host cell. In the lysogenic cycle, viral DNA integrates into the host cell permanently and might remain dormant for periods of time and then result in the lytic cycle.

Chapter Test A

Page 23 • Part A: Multiple Choice

1. D
2. B
3. B

Page 23 • Part B: Matching

Matching Set 1

1. C
2. A
3. B

Matching Set 2

4. B
5. A
6. C

Page 24 • Part C: Interpreting Drawings

1. bacterium
2. A: pilus; B: capsule
3. virus

Page 24 • Part D: Short Answer

1. Round bacteria are called cocci, rod-shaped bacteria are called bacilli, and spiral-shaped bacteria are called spirilli.

2. The virus attaches itself to a cell and uses specific receptors on the plasma membrane. It injects genetic material into the cytoplasm of the host cell, and the material replicates itself inside the cell.

Copyright © Glencoe/McGraw-Hill, a division of The McGraw-Hill Companies, Inc.

Page 25 • Part E: Concept Application

1. Binary fission is the division of a bacterium cell into two identical daughter cells. Moist, warm human tissues create ideal growing conditions for some bacteria, and these conditions can allow bacteria to reproduce every 20 min. Billions of infectious bacteria can be present in a person 24 h after the initial infection.

2. Bacteria are the primary decomposers in a forest ecosystem, and they convert the tissues of dead organisms into vital nutrients in the soil. Without this recycling of nutrients, forest soil would become nutrient-poor causing the death of trees and a collapse of the ecosystem.

Chapter Test B

Page 26 • Part A: Multiple Choice

1. A
2. A
3. B
4. B
5. B

Page 26 • Part B: Matching and Completion

Matching

1. C
2. A
3. B

Completion

4. nucleus
5. coccus
6. bacilli
7. decomposers
8. virus
9. prion

Page 27 • Part C: Interpreting Drawings

1. bacterium
2. A: pilus; B: capsule; C: cell wall; D: plasma membrane
3. virus
4. A: spikes; B: envelop

Page 28 • Part D: Short Answer

1. A Gram stain will classify a bacteria strain into one of two groups. Gram-positive bacteria turn dark purple in the stain, and Gram-negative bacteria appear pink. From this test, the doctor can decide on an appropriate antibiotic to cure the infection.

2. Nitrogen-fixing bacteria take nitrogen from the atmosphere and convert it into nitrogen compounds used by plants. The nitrogen compounds are essential for amino acid production, and the amino acids are converted into proteins. Humans need protein to repair and grow muscle and tissues, and protein originates from the nitrogen compounds made by nitrogen-fixing bacteria.

3. Chemoautotrophs need no light to create energy, and during the process of chemosynthesis, they break down inorganic compounds to acquire energy. Photoautotrophs require light, and they create energy through the process of photosynthesis.

Page 28 • Part E: Concept Application

1. Moist, warm human tissues create ideal growing conditions for bacterial binary fission. Therefore, assuming the bacteria reproduce every 20 min, billions of infectious bacteria will be present in a person 24 h after the initial infection.

2. The bacteria that cause tetanus produce endospores. Although the hot, dry conditions might kill the bacteria cells, the endospores they produce allow their cells to survive the harsh conditions for long periods of time.

Chapter Test C

Page 29 • Part A: Multiple Choice

1. B
2. D
3. D
4. C
5. C
6. D

Copyright © Glencoe/McGraw-Hill, a division of The McGraw-Hill Companies, Inc.

Chapter 18 — Teacher Guide and Answers

Page 29 • Part B: Completion

1. prokaryotes
2. diffusion
3. normal flora
4. mutations
5. lysogenic cycle
6. prion

Page 30 • Part C: Interpreting Drawings

1. bacterium
2. A: pilus; B: capsule; C: cell wall; D: plasma membrane; E: DNA in chromosome
3. virus
4. A: spikes; B: envelop; C: genetic material (DNA or RNA); D: capsule

Page 30 • Part D: Short Answer

1. There are three major groups of archaebacteria including thermoacidophiles, halophiles, and methanogens. Thermoacidophiles live in hot, acidic environments such as hot springs and ocean thermal vents. Halophiles tolerate salty environments such as the Dead Sea, and methanogens live in habitats without oxygen such as wetlands and volcanic vents.

2. Deer browse on forest vegetation, and the trees and other plants of the forest depend on nutrient-rich soil for growth. Decomposing bacteria break down dead organisms into nutrients, and these nutrients are recycled back through the forest ecosystem and used by forest plants.

3. Obligate aerobes use oxygen in metabolic processes to create energy. Obligate anaerobes use the process of fermentation in the absence of oxygen to create energy. Facultative anaerobes use either oxygen-based metabolism or fermentation for energy production, depending on their environment.

Page 31 • Part E: Concept Application

1. A Gram stain must be completed to determine the type of cell wall of the infecting bacteria. Bacteria with large amounts of peptidoglycan in their cell walls will appear dark purple and are called Gram-positive. Bacteria with less peptidoglycan in their cell walls will appear light pink and are referred to as Gram-negative. From this test, the doctor can choose an appropriate antibiotic to cure the infection.

2. Harmful bacteria grow quickly on some foods, such as meats, because they provide a warm, nutrient-rich environment. Using the process of binary fission, a bacterium cell can divide every 20 min under ideal conditions, and the meat will have dangerous levels of bacteria in a matter of hours.

3. All living things are composed of cells, but viruses are made of a protein coat. Viruses cannot become active unless they are inside host cells.

Copyright © Glencoe/McGraw-Hill, a division of The McGraw-Hill Compa

Diagnostic Test

Page 39

1. The correct answer is A. Based on student responses, use the list below to address preconceptions.

   • **Student thinks algae is classified as a plant.** Direct student to the discussion of algae in Section 19.3.

   • **Student thinks protozoans, such as amoebas and parameciums, are classified as animals.** Direct student to the discussion of animal-like protists in Section 19.2.

   • **Student thinks all microscopic organisms such as worms are classified as protists.** Direct student to the introductory discussion of protists in Section 19.1.

   • **Student thinks that rotifers are protists.** Explain that rotifers are the smallest types of animals and they are classified in Kingdom Animalia.

2. The correct answer is D. Based on student responses, use the list below to address preconceptions.

   • **Student confuses funguslike protists with algae.** Direct student to the discussion algae in Section 19.3 and the discussion of funguslike protists in Section 19.4.

   • **Student thinks slime molds and water molds are classified as fungi.** Direct student to the discussion of funguslike protists in Section 19.4.

   • **Student thinks slime molds and water molds are classified as plants.** Direct student to the discussion of funguslike protists in Section 19.4.

3. Not all protists live in freshwater environments. Some live in salt water and others do not live in aquatic environments. Some live in symbiotic relationships with other organisms, while others do not. Based on student responses, use the list below to address preconceptions.

   • **Student thinks freshwater is the only habitat of protists.** Direct student to the discussion of protist habitats in Section 19.1.

   • **Student thinks all protists have an aquatic habitat.** Direct student to the discussion of protist habitats in Section 19.1.

• **Student thinks most or all protists are parasitic in nature living inside host organisms.** Direct student to the discussion of protist habitats in Section 19.1.

Launch Lab

Page 40 • What is a protist?

Analysis

1. Accept all reasonable answers. Brainstorm and develop a class list of characteristics for each category of protist.

2. Students should be able to infer that animal-like protests have structures that enable them to move and capture food, and plantlike protists have structures that enable them to make food.

MiniLab

Page 41 • Investigate Photosynthesis in Algae

Analysis

1. Sample answer: The presence of oxygen bubbles indicates that photosynthesis has occurred.

2. Answers will vary. Algae contain chlorophyll and undergo photosynthesis. Algae require light to photosynthesize. If they are placed in a dark location, they will die.

3. Sample answer: chloroplasts

MiniLab

Page 42 • Investigate Slime Molds

Analysis

1. Answers will depend on the type of slime mold the students received. Acellular slime molds can contain millions of nuclei floating freely in the cytoplasm. The cellular slime molds contain individual cells.

2. Student answers should discuss similarities in structure.

3. Student classifications should make logical, scientific sense.

Copyright © Glencoe/McGraw-Hill, a division of The McGraw-Hill Companies, Inc.

BioLab: Design Your Own

Page 43 • Investigate: How do protozoa behave?

Analyze and Conclude

1. Protozoa are not synthetic; they must take in food; they have a cell membrane.

2. Sample answer: Do protozoa respond to light?

3. Students should restate their initial hypothesis.

4. Check students' data.

5. Accept conclusions that are supported by data.

6. Accept all reasonable responses.

Real-World Biology: Analysis

Page 45 • Algae in Your Foods

Planning the Activity

This activity should be used after students have studied algae in Section 19.3 of the text. It can be used to reinforce the concept of different phyla and species of algae.

Purpose

Students investigate food additives made from algae.

Career Applications

Food science and technology is one of the world's largest industries. As the world's population continues to grow, opportunities for food scientists and technologists grow as well. Technologists in this field work at a variety of tasks such as discovering new food sources and preservation methods, improving consumer food products, and ensuring that the food supply is safe and nutritious. To do this, food technologists use their knowledge of chemistry, microbiology, and other sciences to develop new or better ways of preserving, processing, packaging, storing, and delivering food. Many food technologists work in product development. Others enforce government regulations—inspecting food processing areas and making sure that sanitation, safety, quality, and waste management standards are met.

Teaching Strategies

- Introduce the activity by asking students "Have you ever eaten algae?" If they say no, ask "Have you ever eaten yogurt, cheese, or ice cream?" Some students might know that algae are common ingredients in Asian recipes, and some might know that products from algae are typically added to foods as thickening agents.

- After students have read the opening paragraphs and studied **Table 1,** have them identify how the algae in **Figures 1–3** are used.

- Below Level: Be sure students understand how varied the different phyla of algae are and that each phylum includes many different species.

- Above Level: Have interested students find out more about the uses of algae or make recipes using algae.

Answers to the Student Worksheet

Analyze and Conclude

1. Student answers will vary but should include foods that are made with algae or food additives made from algae.

2. *Laminaria, Undaria,* and *Porphyra* are the genera used most often as foods.

3. Jelly-like desserts could be made with agar instead of gelatin because agar is a substitute for gelatin and is used for thickening.

4. Because people in Japan and the islands in the Pacific Ocean live close to coastal water, they have easier access to algae than do people living in Arizona and New Mexico. People living in dry areas have been eating algae only since the technology for shipping algae was developed.

5. Making food additives from algae is desirable because algae are nutritious and abundant.

Careers in Biology

Food technologists use their knowledge of chemistry, microbiology, and other sciences to develop new or better ways of preserving, processing, packaging, storing, and delivering food.

Enrichment

Page 47 • Impact of Protists on Humans

Student presentations will vary but should be accurate and complete, including information about the protist's impact on humans and any eradication methods that have been used. Photographs of the protist and diagrams of its life cycle would be useful illustrations for the presentations.

Copyright © Glencoe/McGraw-Hill, a division of The McGraw-Hill Companies, Inc.

Concept Mapping

Page 48 • The Classification of Protists

1. protists
2. protozoans
3. algae
4. food
5. slime molds
6. ciliates
7. sporozoans
8. nutrients
9. cilia
10. pseudopods
11. flagella

Study Guide

Page 49 • Section 19.1

1. E
2. D
3. C
4. A
5. B
6. food source
7. amoeba
8. food
9. heterotroph
10. kelp
11. autotroph
12. evolutionary history
13. endosymbiosis

Page 50 • Section 19.2

1. cilia
2. micronucleus
3. contractile vacuole
4. oral groove
5. macronucleus
6. Apicomplexa
7. Zoomastigina
8. Ciliophora
9. Sarcodina

10. Apicomplexa, Zoomastigina
11. Chagas' disease is a type of sleeping sickness, also called American sleeping sickness. A zooflagellate causes the disease.
12. African sleeping sickness is transmitted to humans by the bite of a tsetse fly.

Page 51 • Section 19.3

1. food
2. true
3. dinoflagellates
4. true
5. euglenoids
6. brown algae
7. true
8. true
9. sporophyte
10. spores
11. gametophytes
12. gametes

Page 52 • Section 19.4

1. chitin
2. plasmodium
3. acrasin
4. Myxomycota
5. Oomycota
6. *Phytophthora infestans*
7. cellular slime mold
8. acellular slime mold
9. false
10. true

Guía de estudio

Página 53 • Sección 19.1

1. E
2. D
3. C
4. A
5. B
6. fuente alimenticia
7. ameba

Copyright © Glencoe/McGraw-Hill, a division of The McGraw-Hill Companies, Inc.

8. alimento

9. heterótrofo

10. kelp

11. autótrofo

12. historia evolutiva

13. endosimbiosis

Página 54 • Sección 19.2

1. cilio

2. micronúcleo

3. vacuola contráctil

4. hendidura oral

5. macronúcleo

6. Aplicomplejos

7. Zoomastiginos

8. Ciliados

9. Sarcodinos

10. Aplicomplejos, Zoomastiginos

11. La enfermedad de Chagas es un tipo de enfermedad del sueño, también conocida como enfermedad americana de sueño. Un zooflagelado causa la enfermedad.

12. La enfermedad africana del sueño se transmite a los humanos mediante la picadura de la mosca tsé-tsé.

Página 55 • Sección 19.3

1. del alimento

2. verdadero

3. dinoflagelados

4. verdadero

5. euglenoides

6. alga café

7. verdadero

8. verdadero

9. esporofitos

10. esporas

11. gametofitos

12. gametos

Página 56 • Sección 19.4

1. quitina

2. plasmodio

3. acrasina

4. Mixomicetes

5. Oomicetes

6. *Phytophthora infestans*

7. moho limoso celular

8. moho limoso acelular

9. falso

10. verdadero

Section Quick Check

Page 57 • Section 19.1

1. Protists are usually found in damp or aquatic environments such as ponds, streams, oceans, decaying leaves, and damp soil.

2. To be classified in Kingdom Protista, an organism must be a eukaryote and cannot be classified as an animal, a plant, or a fungus.

3. Protists are currently grouped by how they obtain nutrients. This method does not take into account future discoveries about the evolutionary history of the organisms now called protists.

4. The theory of endosymbiosis states that certain organelles, such as mitochondria and chloroplasts, evolved from free-living bacteria. Photosynthetic protists evolved from cells in which a photosynthetic bacterium lived in a mutualistic relationship.

5. Protists and certain of their organelles evolved from archaebacteria and eubacteria.

Page 58 • Section 19.2

1. Biologists classify protozoans by their method of movement.

2. Amoebas are enveloped in two membranes—an outer plasma membrane and an inner stiff membrane called ectoplasm. Inside the outer membrane is the cytoplasm, which contains a nucleus, food vacuoles, and sometimes a contractile vacuole.

3. Cilia are short, hairlike projections from cells. Numerous cilia occur on a ciliated cell. Flagella are long, whiplike projections from cells. A cell will normally have only a few flagella. Both are used for propelling a unicellular organism through water. Cilia are also used for pulling food into the cell.

Copyright © Glencoe/McGraw-Hill, a division of The McGraw-Hill Companies, Inc.

Chapter 19 — *Teacher Guide and Answers*

4. Sarcodines are more like sporozoans because they both lack cilia and flagella. Also, in sarcodines and sporozoans, respiration and excretion occur by diffusion through the plasma membrane.

5. Paramecia that live in freshwater have contractile vacuoles, which collect excess water and expel it from the cell. In freshwater, water constantly enters the cell by osmosis. A paramecium that lives in the ocean would not need a contractile vacuole if the concentration of dissolved substances in the water were greater than the concentration of dissolved substances in the cell. In this case, the paramecium would continually lose water by osmosis.

Page 59 • Section 19.3

1. Scientists classify algae by the types of chlorophyll and secondary pigments, the method of food storage, and the composition of the cell wall.

2. Green algae contain chlorophyll as a primary photosynthetic pigment, giving them a green color; they have cells walls; and they store their food as carbohydrates.

3. In algae that have alternation of generations, a haploid stage (generation) called a gametophyte produces gametes. When two gametes fuse, a diploid stage (generation) called a sporophyte develops. Cells in the sporophyte undergo meiosis and produce haploid spores, which grow into a new gametophyte. This life cycle take two generations to complete, and a haploid generation alternates with a diploid generation.

4. Diatoms store food as oil, while other types of algae store food as carbohydrates.

5. Algae are important sources of food for humans. Unicellular algae, or phytoplankton, form the foundation of most food webs that involve humans. Algae are also an important source of atmospheric oxygen, which humans need for respiration.

Page 60 • Section 19.4

1. Water molds and downy mildews live in water or damp places.

2. In the nineteenth century, the downy mildew *Phytophthora infestans* infected and destroyed the potato crop of Ireland. This caused the population of the United States to increase when a large number of people emigrated from Ireland to escape the famine that resulted.

3. The slime molds in the phylum Myoxmycota are acellular because they go through a phase in their life cycle in which the nucleus divides but no internal cell walls form. The result is a mass of cytoplasm with multiple nuclei.

4. Fungi and slime molds both use spores to reproduce, feed on decaying organic matter, and absorb nutrients through their cell walls. However, the cell walls of fungi contain chitin, whereas the cell walls of slime molds do not.

5. The motile mass of an acellular slime mold contains many diploid nuclei but no separate cells. The mass of a cellular slime mold is a congregation of haploid amoeba-like cells that forms a sluglike colony.

Chapter Test A

Page 61 • Part A: Multiple Choice

1. B
2. C
3. B

Page 61 • Part B: Matching

Matching Set 1

1. D
2. C
3. B
4. A

Matching Set 2

5. B
6. C
7. A

Page 62 • Part C: Interpreting Drawings and Graphs

1. The Stentor is classified in phylum Ciliophora because it has cilia. It has hairlike cilia ringing its mouth area to create small currents for drawing food into its mouth.

2. Currently, scientists believe photosynthesizing protists evolved when ancestors of present-day algae engulfed photosynthesizing bacteria and the two organisms formed a more complex organism capable of photosynthesis. Chloroplasts became a part of photosynthetic protists.

3. Because they diverged from a common ancestor shared by halophiles and methanogens, thermophiles have remained relatively unchanged throughout their evolutionary history.

Page 63 • Part D: Short Answer

1. The organism must be a eukaryote, and it cannot be classified as an animal, plant, or fungi.

2. Sea lettuce takes two generations to complete its life cycle. During one generation, the algae reproduces sexually, and during the next generation it reproduces asexually.

Page 63 • Part E: Concept Application

1. Animal-like protists ingest food and usually possess structures for facilitating movement. Plantlike protists manufacture their own food using the process of photosynthesis, and they do not have structures for movement. Funguslike protists absorb nutrients from other organisms and have no structures for movement.

2. Possible slime molds habitats include shaded, decaying (leaf litter) leaves and rotting logs.

Chapter Test B

Page 64 • Part A: Multiple Choice

1. B
2. B
3. B
4. A
5. C

Page 64 • Part B: Matching and Completion

Matching

1. B
2. D
3. A
4. E

Completion

5. Euglenophyta
6. dinoflagellates
7. Chlorophyta
8. brown algae
9. diatoms
10. red algae

Page 65 • Part C: Interpreting Drawings and Graphs

1. The Stentor is classified in phylum Ciliophora because it has cilia. It has hairlike cilia ringing its mouth area to create small currents for drawing food into its mouth.

2. Both types of protists evolved mitochondria after their ancestors assimilated purple bacteria, but only photosynthesizing protists assimilated photosynthesizing bacteria and contain chloroplasts, which give them the ability to produce their own food.

3. All protists might be photosynthesizing protists because they all would have evolved chloroplasts.

Page 66 • Part D: Short Answer

1. Both ciliates and sporozoans reproduce asexually. Sporozoans maintain genetic variation through sexual reproduction; ciliates create genetic variation through the sexual process of conjugation, which involves a DNA exchange between two individuals. Sporozoans require multiple hosts to complete their life cycles; ciliates require no hosts for reproduction.

2. Sea lettuce takes two generations to complete its life cycle. During one generation, the algae reproduces sexually, and during the next generation, it reproduces asexually.

Copyright © Glencoe/McGraw-Hill, a division of The McGraw-Hill Companies, Inc.

3. Both slime molds and fungi use spores for reproduction, and they both absorb nutrients by feeding on dead, organic matter. Fungi have cell walls composed of chitin; the cell walls of slime molds lack chitin.

Page 66 • Part E: Concept Application

1. Nutrient-rich ocean water and other favorable environmental conditions cause dinoflagellate populations to increase dramatically and create red tide. Human activities, such as agricultural or fertilizer runoff that add excess nutrients to ocean water, can contribute to red tide.

2. Diatoms and other plantlike protists create food and oxygen through the process of photosynthesis. If plantlike protists die in large numbers, ocean food chains could be disrupted and atmospheric oxygen levels could decrease.

3. A downy mildew infected and destroyed Irish potatoes. Because the potato was their primary food source and Irish peasants could not afford other agricultural products, famine ensued. Prior to the famine, Irish farmers could have diversified the crops they grew. Students also might comment on the social action of the British government. Accept reasonable hypotheses.

Chapter Test C

Page 67 • Part A: Multiple Choice

1. A
2. B
3. B
4. C
5. D
6. C

Page 67 • Part B: Completion

1. conjugation
2. Apicomplexa
3. Euglenophyta
4. abrasive or filtering agent
5. chitin
6. water molds

Page 68 • Part C: Interpreting Drawings and Graphs

1. The Stentor is classified in phylum Ciliophora because it has cilia. It has hairlike cilia ringing its mouth area to create small currents for drawing food into its mouth.

2. Mitochondria are common to all protists, but chloroplasts are only common to plantlike protists. Had chloroplasts been assimilated into protists before mitochondria, most or all protists would be capable of photosynthesis, and protist phyla would not possess mitochondria.

3. Mitochondria are different from other organelles. They have a unique structure and possess as distinct DNA that is more similar to prokaryotic DNA than to eukaryotic nuclear DNA.

Page 69 • Part D: Short Answer

1. Animal-like protists are heterotrophs and ingest food; plantlike protists use photosynthesis to produce food, and funguslike protists absorb nutrients from other organisms or organic matter.

2. Paramecium are unicellular protists enclosed by a layer of membrane called a pellicle. A layer of cytoplasm called the ectoplasm lies directly below the pellicle, and cylindrical bodies called trichocysts are embedded in the ectoplasm. Hairlike structures called cilia cover the organism.

3. Ciliates propel themselves through water using small, hairlike structures called cilia that cover their bodies. Sarcodines use cytoplasm extensions called pseudopods to pull themselves along solid substrates. Apicomplexans are parasitic and have no method of location. Zooflagellates use a whiplike structure called a flagella to move through water.

4. The primary pigment of Chlorophytes is chlorophyll, which gives them a green color, and they are called green algae. They grow as unicellular, colonies of cells, or multicellular organisms. Phaeophytes are brown algae and get their color from the pigment fucoxanthin, and most of them form large multicellular, plantlike organisms. Rhodophytes have pigments called phycobilins, which give them a red color, and they are multicellular red alga.

Copyright © Glencoe/McGraw-Hill, a division of The McGraw-Hill Companies, Inc.

Chapter 19 | Teacher Guide and Answers

1. The life cycle of zooflagellates in genus *Trypanosoma* involves two hosts—the tsetse fly and humans. Inside humans, the protists cause African sleeping sickness. Possible solutions to the spread of the disease would be to control the tsetse fly population or deter the insects from biting humans. These measures might include the use of insecticides in tsetse fly habitats, insect repellent by potential human hosts, or releasing tsetse fly predators into the fly's habitat. Drugs or diet changes might also be used to make human blood unpalatable to tsetse flies.

2. The stored oil inside diatoms makes them buoyant enabling them to float on the surface of oceans. On ocean surfaces, they photosynthesize and produce large quantities of the biosphere's oxygen. Without stored oil, diatoms would sink, be unable to photosynthesize, and die. This would result in a significant loss of Earth's oxygen supply. Ocean food chains would also be disrupted because diatom oil is a nutritious food source for many marine organisms.

Copyright © Glencoe/McGraw-Hill, a division of The McGraw-Hill Companies, Inc.

Diagnostic Test

Page 77

1. The correct answer is C. Based on student responses, use the list below to address preconceptions.

   • **Student thinks lichen is a plant.** Direct student to the ecology of fungi discussion in Section 20.3.

   • **Student thinks fungi perform photosynthesis.** Direct student to the introducing fungi discussion in Section 20.1.

   • **Student thinks fungi have plantlike structures such as roots.** Direct student to the major features of fungi discussion in Section 20.1.

   • **Student thinks the fruiting body of mushrooms is the primary body structure instead of the reproductive structure.** Direct student to the major features of fungi discussion in Section 20.1.

   • **Student misidentifies moss or slime mold as fungi.** Explain that moss is a simple plant and refer student to Chapter 19 to review the types of fungi-like protists such as slime molds.

2. The correct answer is D. Based on student responses, use the list below to address preconceptions.

   • **Student thinks fungi use only sexual reproduction.** Direct student to the reproduction in fungi discussion in Section 20.1.

   • **Student thinks fungi reproduce using sperm and egg cells as animals do.** Direct student to the reproduction in fungi discussion in Section 20.1.

   • **Student thinks fungi use only asexual reproduction.** Direct student to the reproduction in fungi discussion in Section 20.1.

   • **Student thinks fungi reproduce using seeds.** Direct student to the reproduction in fungi discussion in Section 20.1.

   • **Student thinks fungi use reproductive structures other than spores.** Direct student to the reproduction in fungi discussion in Section 20.1.

3. Though mold spoils food and sometimes makes people sick, not all fungi are bad. Some fungi are used to make medicine, and some fungi, such as mushrooms, yeast, and some molds, are used for food. Based on student responses, use the list below to address preconceptions.

   • **Student thinks all fungi are harmful.** Introduce student to some of the beneficial uses for fungi and direct student to the fungi and humans discussion in Section 20.3.

   • **Student thinks mushrooms are the only edible fungi.** Direct student to the fungi and humans discussion in Section 20.3.

   • **Student is unaware of the medical applications of mold and other fungi.** Remind student that drugs such as penicillin are made from fungi. Direct student to the fungi and humans discussion in Section 20.3.

   • **Student thinks all fungi attack and decompose organic matter.** Direct student to the nutrition in fungi discussion in Section 20.1 and the mycorrhizae discussion in Section 20.3.

   • **Student thinks fungi are used to make all cheeses.** Direct student to the fungi and humans discussion in Section 20.3.

   • **Student does not recognize yeast as fungi.** Direct student to the sac fungi discussion in Section 20.2.

Launch Lab

Page 78 • What differences exist among fungi?

Analyze and Conclude

1. Fungi probably varied in size, color, odor, physical structure, and nutrient source.

2. Possible answer: Most fungi seem to produce a powdery substance (spores) and be made of filaments.

MiniLab

Page 79 • Examine Yeast Growth

Analysis

1. The greater the availability of sugar, the greater the yeast reproduction.

2. Yeast can obtain energy through anaerobic respiration, so though growth may slow, the yeast would not die until the sugar ran out.

Copyright © Glencoe/McGraw-Hill, a division of The McGraw-Hill Companies, Inc.

MiniLab

Page 80 • Investigate Mold Growth

Analysis

1. the slice without the added salt
2. Yes, it slowed mold growth.

BioLab

Page 81 • How do environmental factors affect mold growth?

Analyze and Conclude

1. Answers will vary. The independent variable is based on the environmental factor the student chooses to investigate. The dependent variable is the rate of mold growth over time.
2. Answers will vary.
3. Answers will vary, but should include a list of conditions the student held the same for each trial.
4. Answers will vary.
5. Answers will vary depending on the students' hypotheses.
6. Possible answer: When the cotton swab is used to introduce the mold to the gelatin, nutrients from the food source are also introduced. To decrease the amount transferred, only a limited amount of food should be introduced to the mold.

Real-World Biology: Lab

Page 83 • Controlling Mold Growth

Planning the Activity

This activity should be used after students have studied the concepts of fungi nutrition and reproduction in Section 20.1 of the text. It can be used to reinforce the traits of common molds in Section 20.2.

Purpose

Students conduct a simple experiment to determine environmental factors that affect mold growth.

Career Applications

The scientific methods addressed in this activity are similar to those used in the food industry to solve problems in research and development. The food industry also evaluates food manufacturing,

processing, and packaging programs in order to advise companies on food protection. Food science technicians set up, operate, and maintain laboratory instruments; monitor experiments; make observations; calculate and record results; and often develop conclusions. They might test a food's susceptibility or resistance to contamination by outside agents, such as bacteria and fungi, and assist in package design to keep contamination at a minimum. Technicians who work in production monitor manufacturing processes and might be involved in quality control by testing products for proper proportions of ingredients, purity, strength, and shelf life.

Materials Tips

Materials sliced white bread from a bakery (most packaged bread contains preservatives that inhibit mold growth), petri dishes with lids, tape, marker, droppers, water, refrigerator

- Self-sealing bags can be substituted for the petri dishes.
- It can take four to seven days for mold to appear. You might want to have students begin the activity toward the end of the week so that they can observe mold growth the following week.

Safety Tips

- Students should wash their hands both before and after they make their daily observations.
- Warn students to leave the lids taped on the dishes. Some students could have allergies to the mold spores.

Teaching Strategies

- Have students work in groups of three or four. Introduce the activity by asking students "Do you know the names of any undesirable household fungi?" (Suggest mildew and bread mold if they do not know.) "Where do you think the fungi in your home come from?"
- After students have read the opening paragraphs, have them discuss some possible ways in which fungal growth might be controlled.
- Students should move both petri dishes to the cold environment as soon as they observe fungal growth in any of the four dishes. Because early signs of mold growth are difficult to see, it might be necessary for students to make their daily observations with a magnifying lens.

Copyright © Glencoe/McGraw-Hill, a division of The McGraw-Hill Companies, Inc.

- Have interested students learn more about mold growth in homes.
- Below Level: Help students understand why water is important to mold growth by having them think about their own need for water. Explain that all living things need water to survive and grow.
- Above Level: Have students design an experiment to test the effects of another variable on mold growth. For example, they could compare regular bacon with low-salt bacon. Depending on time available, they could conduct the experiment or write the design.

Answers to the Student Worksheet

Analyze and Conclude

1. The petri dishes containing water (B and D) showed the greatest mold growth. Of these two, the petri dish placed in the warm environment (B) should show greater growth at the end of the experiment.

2. Most students will find that the dry bread pieces showed little or no mold growth. Fungi need moisture to thrive.

3. Students should recognize that fungal spores fill the air, and that if the bread is not covered overnight, spores could land on the bread. The reproductive strategy of fungi is to spread out quickly over large areas.

4. Most students will find that low temperatures inhibited mold growth.

5. Students should infer that keeping foods covered, dry, and cool is important for inhibiting the growth of mold. Some students might infer that keeping a home dry (lowering humidity, fixing leaks, wiping up standing water, drying out wet areas) can help inhibit mold growth.

6. Students should recognize that drying and salting reduce the amount of water available for fungal growth. Canning prevents the introduction of fungal spores and kills existing spores by heating them. Freezing inhibits the growth of fungal spores because of the low temperature.

Careers in Biology

Food science technicians set up, operate, and maintain laboratory instruments; monitor experiments; make observations; calculate and record results; and

often develop conclusions. They might test a food's susceptibility or resistance to contamination and assist in package design. Some technicians might be involved in quality control by testing products for proper proportions of ingredients, purity, strength, and shelf life.

Enrichment

Page 85 • Effects of Fungi

Student articles will vary, but they should be accurate and clearly written. All questions posed in the class discussions should be thoroughly researched, and answers should be supported by data and research. All sources should be accurately cited.

Concept Mapping

Page 86 • Feeding Relationships of Fungi

1. saprophytic
2. parasitic
3. mutualistic
4. living hosts
5. mutualistic relationship
6. haustoria
7. waste matter
8. dead organisms
9. raw materials
10. other organisms

Study Guide

Page 87 • Section 20.1

1. C
2. D
3. B
4. E
5. A
6. Parasitic Fungi
7. Mutualistic Fungi
8. Saprophytic Fungi, Parasitic Fungi, Mutualistic Fungi
9. Saprophytic Fungi
10. Mutualistic Fungi
11. asexually

Copyright © Glencoe/McGraw-Hill, a division of The McGraw-Hill Companies, Inc.

12. survival

13. wind

14. Sporangia

15. meiosis

Page 88 • Section 20.2

1. E

2. D

3. C

4. A

5. B

6. spores

7. rhizoids

8. stolons

9. mating strains

10. sporangia

11. rhizoids

12. spores

13. stolons

14. sporangia

15. mating strains

16. C

17. B

18. B

19. A

20. B

21. B

22. C

23. caps

24. basidium

25. spores

Page 90 • Section 20.3

Mycorrhizae: 1, 3, 7; Lichens: 2, 4, 8;
Both: 5, 6

9. immune suppressant (antirejection)

10. true

11. Fermentation

12. bioremediation

Guía de estudio

Página 91 • Sección 20.1

1. C

2. D

3. B

4. E

5. A

6. Hongos parasíticos

7. Hongos mutualistas

8. Hongos saprofitos, Hongos parasíticos, Hongos mutualistas

9. Hongos saprofitos

10. Hongos mutualistas

11. asexualmente

12. supervivencia

13. viento

14. esporangios

15. meiosis

Página 92 • Sección 20.2

1. E

2. D

3. C

4. A

5. B

6. esporas

7. rizoides

8. estolones

9. cepas fecundantes

10. esporangios

11. rizoides

12. esporas

13. estolones

14. esporangios

15. cepas fecundantes

16. C

17. B

18. A

19. A

20. A

Copyright © Glencoe/McGraw-Hill, a division of The McGraw-Hill Companies, Inc.

21. A

22. B

23. capuchones

24. basidio

25. esporas

Página 94 • Sección 20.3

Micorrizas: 1, 3, 7; Líquenes: 2, 4, 8; Ambos: 5, 6

9. inmunosupresor (antirrechazo)

10. verdadero

11. fermentación

12. biorremediación

Section Quick Check

Page 95 • Section 20.1

1. Most fungi are multicellular, but yeasts are unicellular.

2. Fungi absorb nutrient molecules from their surroundings. The extensive hyphae of multicellular fungi provide a larger surface area for absorbing nutrients. As the number and length of the hyphae increase, the surface area from which the fungus can absorb nutrients also increases.

3. Possible response: The body of a multicellular fungus consists of a mass of hyphae called a mycelium, which forms fruiting bodies for reproduction.

4. Spores are reproductive structures that grow into a new individual. Sporophores are the structures that produce fungal spores.

5. Saprophytic fungi are decomposers that recycle nutrients from dead organisms and prevent animal carcasses, dead plant material, and other organic matter from littering the surface of Earth.

Page 96 • Section 20.2

1. Fungi are divided into phyla based on structure and methods of reproduction.

2. The phylum Chytridiomycota contains only unicellular fungi.

3. An ascocarp is the sporophore of an ascomycete, which produces ascospores in a saclike ascus. A basidiocarp is the sporophore of a basidiomycete, which produces basidiospores in a club-shaped basidium.

4. Sexual reproduction in fungi involves hyphae from two different mating strains. The mating strains are termed plus (+) and minus (−) instead of male and female. Parts of the two haploid hyphae fuse to form a diploid cell that later divides by meiosis, forming haploid spores.

5. Deuteromycetes are reclassified into different phyla of fungi when their sexual reproductive structures are observed. Most deuteromycetes that have been reclassified are ascomycetes. Eventually, the number of species of deuteromycetes will decrease and the number of species of ascomycetes will increase.

Page 97 • Section 20.3

1. Lichens and mycorrhizae are two types of mutualistic relationships that involve fungi.

2. Mycorrhizae are beneficial to plants because they increase the surface area from which water and other nutrients are absorbed from the soil. They also absorb and concentrate various minerals for the plant.

3. Bioremediation is the use of microorganisms to remove environmental pollutants. The fungi are mixed with water or soil, where they decompose organic materials in the pollutants.

4. The fungus provides a dense protective web of hyphae in which the alga (also called cyanobacterium) can grow. The alga produces food used by both organisms.

5. The harmful fungi are parasites that live on other living organisms. They reduce the populations of some organisms by killing the weakest individuals.

Chapter Test A

Page 98 • Part A: Multiple Choice

1. B

2. A

3. C

Page 98 • Part B: Matching

1. B

2. A

3. C

Copyright © Glencoe/McGraw-Hill, a division of The McGraw-Hill Companies, Inc.

Chapter 20 | Teacher Guide and Answers

Page 99 • Part C: Interpreting Drawings

1. A: stipe; B: cap; C: gills
2. A: basidium; B: bisidiospore; C: hypha
3. The basidia produce basidiospores that fall to the ground. When conditions are right, the basidiospores develop into new hyphae.

Page 99 • Part D: Short Answer

1. Saprophytic fungi decompose dead organisms to absorb nutrients. Parasitic fungi absorb nutrients directly from the living cells of another organism. Mutualistic fungi have mutually beneficial relationships with plants or algae.
2. Lichen is a type of symbiotic relationship between a fungus and either a green alga or cyanobacterium.

Page 100 • Part E: Concept Application

1. Both plants and fungi have cells with cell walls, but fungi cell walls are composed of chitin, while plant cell walls are made of cellulose. Fungi are made of threadlike filaments called hyphae, and they do not have the same types of body parts as plants, such as roots, leaves, and stems. Unlike most plants, fungi obtain nutrients from other organisms, not photosynthesis. Most fungi have cross-walls called septas that divide individual cells; plant cells do not have septas.
2. A bioindicator is an organism that is sensitive to environmental changes, and it will be the first to respond to these changes. Lichens are bioindicators because they absorb nutrients directly from the air, making them sensitive to an increase in air pollution levels. Biologists can monitor the health of forest lichen to measure the impact of the pollution created by the new town.

Chapter Test B

Page 101 • Part A: Multiple Choice

1. B
2. D
3. C
4. A

Page 101 • Part B: Matching and Completion

Matching

1. B
2. A
3. C

Completion

4. Chytridiomycota
5. Basidiomycota
6. Ascomycota
7. Zygomycota

Page 102 • Part C: Interpreting Drawings

1. A: stipe; B: cap; C: gills. The gills produce spores for reproducing new mushrooms.
2. The environmental conditions that promote the growth of the basidiocarp include shady places with rich soil, such as forests, and moist conditions after a rainfall.
3. A: basidium; B: basidiospore; C: hypha

Page 103 • Part D: Short Answer

1. Fungi are made of threadlike filaments called hypae. Hyphae branch out as they grow to form a netlike mass called a mycelium. The visible body part above the ground is called the fruiting body, and it is designed for reproduction.
2. Saprophytic fungi are decomposers that break down dead organisms into nutrients. These fungi help recycle nutrients throughout the ecosystem, and they assist in the removal of dead organic matter from the forest floor.
3. Puffballs produce trillions of spores ensuring that some spores will not be found by predators but find favorable growing conditions. Puffball spores are small and lightweight for easy dispersal by small animals or the wind, and the cell walls of the spores resist damage, water loss, and temperature extremes.

Page 103 • Part E: Concept Application

1. Stolons are a type of mold hyphae that spread across the surface of foods. Rhizoids are hyphae that penetrate into foods to absorb nutrients. The chemical would prevent rhizoid hyphae from growing into the center of the bread, but the stolon hyphae would cover the bread's surface.

Copyright © Glencoe/McGraw-Hill, a division of The McGraw-Hill Companies, Inc.

2. Some fungi species decompose the organic molecules in pollutants. Fungi can be mixed with polluted water to detoxify the pollutants in the water. The process of using microorganisms to remove environmental pollutants is called bioremediation.

3. Some fungal species infect and kill trees, such as the fungus that kills American elm trees. If a fungus infects trees harvested for timber, it could adversely affect the timber industry killing trees that could potentially be harvested for profit.

Chapter Test C

Page 104 • Part A: Multiple Choice

1. C
2. A
3. B
4. A
5. D
6. C

Page 104 • Part B: Completion

1. yeast
2. hyphae
3. mycorrhizae
4. septa
5. stolons
6. mycorrhizasymbiosis

Page 105 • Part C: Interpreting Drawings

1. The structure is called a basidiocarp, which is the fruiting body of this mushroom, and its function is reproduction. The stipe of the mushroom raises the cap above the ground. The mushroom's cap protects the gills, and the gills produce spores for reproducing new mushrooms.

2. The long tube-shaped structures producing the spores are called basidia; the spores are called basidiospores, and the underground structure is a hypha.

Page 105 • Part D: Short Answer

1. The cell walls of fungi are composed of a strong, flexible polysaccharide called chitin.

2. All fungi are heterotrophs incapable of photosynthesis. Saprophytic fungi decompose organic matter and absorb nutrients from dead organisms. Parasitic fungi absorb nutrients from living hosts. Mutualistic fungi obtain nutrients from a photosynthesizing, symbiotic partner such as a plant or alga.

3. The sporangium is a sac that produces and protects spores in some fungi species such as black bread mold. If the sporangium of a fungus is damaged, the fungus could lose its ability to produce spores, or if the sporangium can no longer protect spores, the spores could dry out before moist, favorable conditions allowed them to grow.

Page 106 • Part E: Concept Application

1. A fungus is composed of a netlike mass called a mycelium, which is made of flexible threadlike filaments called hyphae. Most or all of this fungi structure remains underground. The bright yellow mushrooms are called the fruiting body of the fungi, and the moist conditions created a favorable environment for the fruiting bodies to grow and reproduce. The fruiting bodies grow by enlarging their structures, and they disperse spores to be spread by the wind or animals.

2. Lichens serve as bioindicators for tundra ecosystems. A bioindicator is an organism that is sensitive to environmental changes and is among the first organisms to respond to the changes. Because they take in nutrients directly from the air, lichens are sensitive to air pollutants. Just as the death of canaries served as a warning to miners that toxic gases were building up in a mineshaft, the death of lichens on the tundra or other remote areas is a warning of degrading air quality.

3. Scientists could identify lichen species most susceptible to air pollutants and monitor these species in various ecosystems worldwide. By periodically evaluating the global health of these lichens, scientists could evaluate the effects and extent of atmospheric pollutants. From their observations and measurements, scientists could create baseline data to use as a warning system for Earth's nations of the potential consequences of increasing air pollution levels.

Copyright © Glencoe/McGraw-Hill, a division of The McGraw-Hill Companies, Inc.

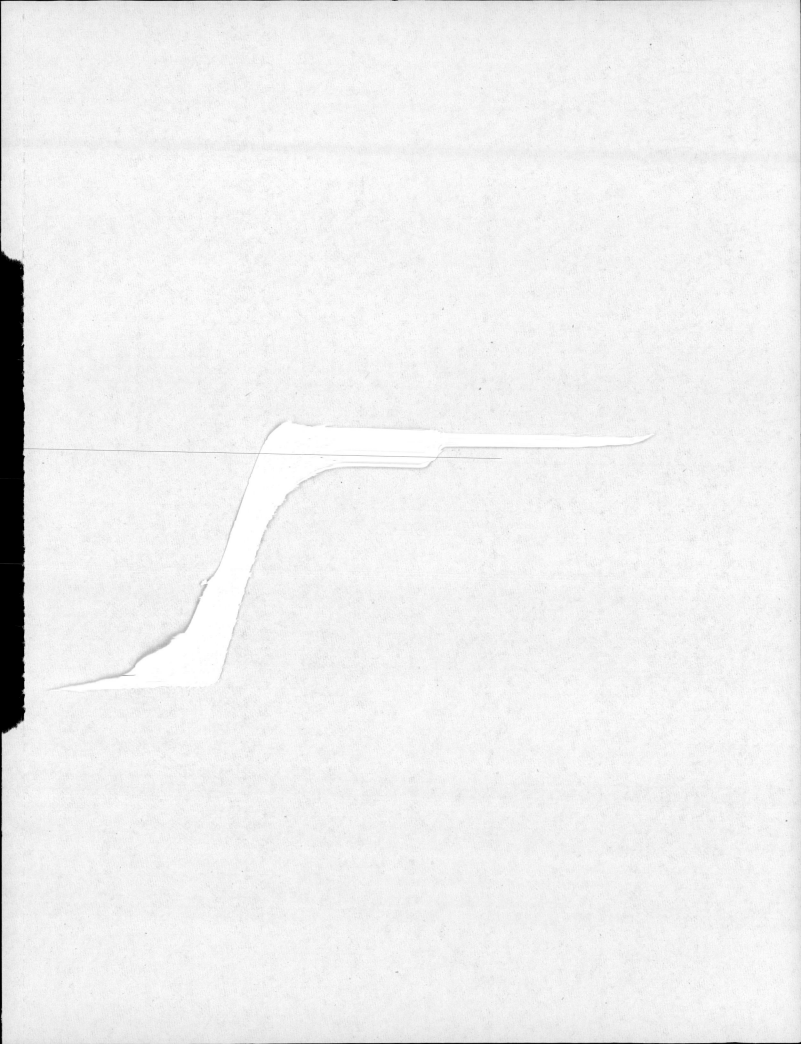